D1268071

WOMEN OF MARRAKECH

Leonora Peets with a woman of Marrakech, 1930.

LEONORA PEETS

Women of Marrakech

Record of a Secret Sharer
1930-1970

TRANSLATED FROM THE ESTONIAN BY
REIN TAAGEPERA

WITH AN INTRODUCTION BY
STEPHEN W. FOSTER

DUKE UNIVERSITY PRESS
DURHAM, NORTH CAROLINA

First published 1988

Published in the UK by
C. Hurst & Company, London

Published in the USA by Duke University Press
Durham, North Carolina

The stories by Leonora Peets were published in Estonian in 1983
by Välis-Eesti, Stockholm, with the title *Maroko taeva all*

Printed in England on long-life paper
at the University Printing House, Oxford

Library of Congress Cataloging-in-Publication Data

Peets, Leonora, 1899–
    [Maroko taeva all. English. Selections]
    Women of Marrakech/Leonora Peets: translated from the Estonian
by Rein Taagepera: with an introduction by Stephen W. Foster.
        p.   cm.
    Translation of: Maroko taeva all.
    Bibliography: p.
    ISBN 0–8223–0812–6
    1. Women——Morocco——Fiction.   I. Title.
PH666.26.E37M313 1988
894′.54532——dc19   87–26536

CONTENTS

TRANSLATOR'S PREFACE

Leonora Peets was born in Tallinn, Estonia, on 25 July 1899, and came to Marrakech in 1929 with her physician husband, Rudolf Peets. They quickly learned the local Arabic and stayed for forty-five years. Mrs Peets published journal articles on Morocco in her native Estonian, which culminated in a book *Maroko taeva all* (Under the Moroccan Sky), Välis-Eesti, Stockholm, 1983. The two main foci of that book, which overlap, could be called 'Women of Marrakech' and 'Physician in Marrakech'.

The pieces in the present selection deal with women; the overlap with the physician's theme is strongest in 'Fatherly Love'. As Mrs Peets' nephew, I spent my high school years (1947–54) in the Peets household in Marrakech — a circumstance that greatly helped me in translating this collection.

Among the several excellent descriptions of Moroccan life, those by Leonora Peets may represent the longest 'time series' by a non-French Western resident. Written over a span of forty years, these stories make the change in local mood palpable, from almost complete female submission in the 1930s ('Apparitions' and 'Children') to open protest by 1970 ('Such a Custom Must be Abolished'). This time-series quality might be unique to Peets, compared to more systematic 'cross-sectional' studies available. Almost without exception, her stories are based on real-life events, reshuffled and reworked mainly to make the protagonists unrecognisable. Having spent six years with Dr and Mrs Peets, I can recognise quite a number of the characters and incidents.

The author is neither a social reformer nor is she a trained anthropologist. She has an eye for detail, a gift for self-expression, longstanding friendships with Moroccan women and men, and no ideological or intellectual axe to grind. As a physician's wife in the Estonian countryside after the First World War, and with some medical training herself, she was not easily shocked by anything she found in Marrakech in 1930. When she was taken aback, she dissected her own reactions dispassionately: what business had she to pass judgment on the customs in Morocco, any more than the German and Russian overlords had in her native Estonia? She is European, and yet she comes from a Finnic population colonised by the European great powers somewhat earlier, before they reached Morocco. She transmits the cry 'Such a custom must be

vii

abolished!' only when it arises on the lips of the women of Marrakech. Meanwhile, over forty years, her job was to observe, understand and describe, sometimes unsparingly and unfashionably, from the viewpoint of a new generation that would prefer to forget about some aspects of past slavery and racism.

School of Social Sciences   REIN TAAGEPERA
University of California, Irvine

SYNOPSIS OF STORIES

'APPARITIONS'
Sidi Mustafa would never allow it, but in his absence his junior wife tells
the servants she is going to pray at a shrine. In reality, she is going on an
even riskier visit, which of course would be perfectly acceptable in a
Western country. (1930)*

'CHILDREN'
Why does the *caid* Omar laugh when he tells about thirty of his forty
children being dead? (1935)

'THE COUSCOUS OF THE DEAD'
The author's gradual discovery of the use of corpses in love magic and in
deadly potions culminates with the story of an orphan: forced to accompany her foster-mother on a grave-opening expedition, she literally takes
a step that wrecks her life. (1938)

'THE BATHS'
At a time when some non-Muslims were chased from public baths with
boiling water, the author was invited to share the bath night of the *cadi*'s
family. She describes the layout of the building, methods used for
washing and depilation, and related social habits and beliefs. (1935)

'WOMAN'S CUNNING'
Two ancient tales are related about a scholar and a *cadi* being fooled by
women. (1935)

'THE SEVENTH WIFE'
A merchant keeps changing wives, as he tries vainly to father a child. At
thirty, he marries for the seventh time; this time the bride is only twelve.
The wedding feast is elaborate (it is described in detail), but soon the
young wife is sent back to her father. Her pretended pregnancy, with
the embryo indefinitely 'asleep', is discounted by a *tbib* (physician) who
does not accept Marrakech folklore. A traffic accident cuts the story
short. (1932)

*The dates indicate the approximate period in which the central action took place, not
when the stories were put in writing.

'MOURNING THE COURT COUNCILLOR'
A widow goes through the funeral ceremony for her husband. (1935)

'ELIMINATION FROM THE HAREM'
The longest story in the collection. After deflating glamorous Western notions about harems, the author introduces a typical harem of a well-to-do Moroccan, with three wives only. The senior wife is middle-class and self-assured, but passive. She remains childless herself, but coopts her own servant, an attractive and submissive girl, as the least dangerous avenue for her husband to have children. He none the less adds a former dancer-musician experienced in the rough-and-tumble of the outside world; she rapidly takes command of the household and has a monopoly on the supply of room keys. But all three wives remain childless.

The month of Ramadan, with absolute fasting during the day and feasting during the night, frays the nerves and exacerbates the continuous tug-of-war between the senior wife and the musician. Their usual audience of servants and poorer relatives is augmented at times through visits from the author, from a woman peddler, and from a Jewess who is indispensable to the secluded harem wives as a go-between. The excitement of the pre-fast celebrations is followed by the unaccustomed hardships of the early days of fast until an ill-tempered routine sets in. Then one of the wives attempts to grab power for herself through witchcraft. The husband almost takes the fateful step over a contraption which is supposed to make him impotent in relation to all other women except the one who has set the trap. But his bare toe touches it, and to make a husband impotent is the worst crime a wife can commit. (1930)

'NEVERMORE'
An angry man may divorce and later reconsider only so many times — and Sidi Mohammed has reached the legal limit. His anger has cooled after the latest dispute, but he cannot remarry his wife, unless. . . . (1945)

'FATHERLY LOVE'
The European *tbib* tries to persuade a farm foreman not to give his daughter yet in marriage, first because she is only eleven and does not yet have menstrual periods, and secondly because the prospective groom has venereal disease. (1955)

'THE FIRST ADDITIONAL WIFE'
Several first wives tell the author of their reactions on learning, suddenly or slowly, that their husbands are going to marry a second wife. (1965)

'AN EX-CHRISTIAN'S SICK VISIT'
Social customs connected with being ill are described along with the non-acceptance of a Frenchwoman converted to Islam. (1965)

'THE GROOM'S VERSION'
A European bride undergoes the traditional wedding ceremony of Marrakech. The groom relates her hesitations, objections and reactions, culminating with a plea: 'Let's leave this place!' (1965)

'THE NAME-GIVING CEREMONY'
Two cousins are married to the same husband. The older one is barren. The name-giving ceremony for the first-born daughter of the younger wife takes its course. Then suddenly the roles of the two wives are altered. (1960)

'SUCH A CUSTOM MUST BE ABOLISHED'
An elderly matron, for the first time ever, bursts out in opposition to age-old customs of female submission: 'No, it is not good that a young girl should be selected for a husband older than her own father!' The women of Marrakech are entering upon a new age. (1970)

GLOSSARY

adoul: notary
afarit: powerful spirit
Aisha-Qandisha: female evil spirit
Aissaoua: Moroccan religious confraternity
akbar: greatest
Allah: God
Allah akbar!: God is greatest
amin: tax collector
ashkoun?: Who is it?
astaghfar Allah!: I beg God's pardon

barakalaoufik: thank you
bastila: pigeon pie made with pastry
beskouit: layer cake
besmellah: in God's name
besmellah rahman rahim: in the name of the gracious and merciful Allah
burnous: traditional male outer garment

cadi: judge
caftan: formal outer garment (female)
caid: local chieftain
casbah: citadel
chikha: professional female dancer
colon: colonial settler (French)
couscous: steamed semolina

darra: co-wife
'darra marra kif defla': 'an additional wife is bitter like the oleander'
defla: oleander
derb: blind alley, *cul de rac*
derbouka: hand drum
Derkaoua: Moroccan religious confraternity
dfina: female outer dress
djellaba: hooded outer garment
Djemaa el-Fna ('place of the head'): principal square in the *medina* of
    Marrakech
djinn, pl. *djnun*: male spirit
djinniyya: female spirit (singular)

El-Aid el-Fitr: feast at the end of Ramadan, also referred to simply as El-Aid
El hamdulillah!: praise be to God

xii

fitna: disorder
fondouk: caravanserai
fota: towel

habiba: friend (female)
hadj: pilgrim to Mecca; also a title
haik: women's white outer garment
hammam: baths
harem: women's living space; 'forbidden'
henna: red dye thought to bring good luck
hetairni: prostitutes (Greek)
hrira: soup taken during the Ramadan fast

inshallah: if God wills

Jehova Sabaoth!: God of Hosts! (Hebrew)

kannel: musical instrument, like zither
kefta: minced meat
khettara: water works
kif: hashish
kohl: eyeliner
Kòran: sacred book of Islam
kouba: woman's room
Koutoubia: great mosque and minaret of Marrakech
kubla: midwife

labes: 'How are you?', 'not bad', 'OK' (literally 'no harm')
La-ilah-illa-Allah, Mo-hammed rasoul Allah!: There is no god but Allah and
    Mohammed is his Prophet
lalla: married woman, honorific
laroussa: bride
Laylat el-Kdar: Night of Fate, 27th day of Ramadan
leffa: viper

makhzen: government
marabout: saint
marbabbik!: welcome
medina: walled town
melh: salt
mellah: Jewish quarter
merroud: case for kohl eyeliner
metboua: forehead ornament
mokhaznees: gendarmes

mouden: prayer caller
moulay: 'lord'; honorific
msakum!: good evening
msalhir!: good afternoon
mzian bzef!: very good

Nasrani, Nazarene: Christian

ouakha: okay

pasha: provincial governor

Rabat: capital city of Morocco
rakas: prayer
Ramadan: Muslim month of fasting
rassoul: clay
roumi: Christian (literally Roman; fem. *roumia*)

Saadian: fifteenth-century Moroccan dynasty
salam!: salutations
salam alik!: peace be with thee (. . . *alikum!*: . . . with you)
Sha'ban: month before Ramadan in Muslim calendar
sherif: descendant of the Prophet
shitan: devil, satan
shuyya: a little; *comme ci, comme ça*
sidi: male honorific
slema: peace be with you; good-bye
souk: market
sultan: ruler
sura: Koranic verse

tajine: stew
taleb: Koranic scholar
Tanja: Tangier
tbib: physician
tbiba: physician's wife
tka'af: paralysing spell
tolba: Koran reciters

umma: the pan-Islamic community

ville nouvelle: new town (French)

yu-yu: ululation
zerneeh: depilatory

INTRODUCTION

By Stephen W. Foster

Morocco had become a rhetorical figure in European discourse even before the advent of colonialism. From the European perspective, it was nearby and thus relatively accessible, yet it remained culturally distinct. It served Europe as a particularisation and exemplar of the exotic, an object of mystery and fascination, a projective screen for European fantasies, and, as in the film *Casablanca*, a locus of intrigue and adventure (Foster 1982). Before and during the colonial period, Morocco was a human landscape exploited by writers and artists such as Pierre Loti Eugène Delacroix (Diehl 1978) and Edith Wharton (1920), who each helped to elaborate what is now referred to as European orientalism (Said 1978). Since colonialism, Morocco has continued to be a favoured image of the still exotic Third World, the destination of a generation of tourists and anthropologists. Throughout this period of changing modes of inter-cultural relations, Morocco — and in particular the place of women in Moroccan society — has been a source of puzzlement for writers, a magnetised object through which they have variously articulated Europe's highly ambivalent, politicised and unstable regard for and relation to the Other.

The writing of Leonora Peets is a striking mixture of ethnography, fiction, narrative and cultural text, a compelling record of a sustained encounter with Moroccan women. *Women of Marrakech* is also an anecdotal portrayal of social change, and at least implicitly a portrait of a European woman coming to terms with foreignness, with Islam, with the exotic, with the Other. Leonora Peets went to Marrakech with her husband, who worked there for many years as a physician. Soon after her arrival she became involved with her neighbours and with her husband's patients. She began to puzzle over and, detective-like, struggle to understand the women around her. Her writing became part of this process. Not with the detached gaze of a mere observer but on the basis of her thoroughgoing participation, Peets' stories expose the fabric, texture and tenor of women's experience in Marrakech.

Hers is a singular voice which speaks in depth of Moroccan women not in the post-colonial present as does Elizabeth Fernea in *A Street in Marrakech* (1975), but throughout a complex historical period during which the political, social and economic enmeshing of Morocco with

1

Europe generated unprecedented challenges and problems for Moroccans. Peets' presence in Marrakech is a moment in and indicator of that enmeshing which brought many changes to Morocco during the years of her residence. Her stories — 'ethnographic fiction' with both a strong narrative apparatus and a readily accessible descriptive effect — are the expression of an historical process which has not yet reached a conclusion and which must be sketched in broad outline in order for the stories to be fully appreciated.

Beginning in the mid-nineteenth century, there was a large-scale influx of European goods and capital into Morocco. Over the succeeding decades, this had the cumulative effect of putting Morocco into enormous debt to Europe, with far-reaching social and political consequences for the country itself. The sultanate was weakened and destabilised. The local rivalries which characterised earlier periods of Moroccan history were again exacerbated. During this same period, internally initiated attempts to reform the old administrative apparatus succeeded in hastening its demise. The government failed to establish a new structure, which only created more social and political divisiveness (Burke 1976). These changes led to the intervention of European powers and set in motion the French colonial offensive after the turn of the century. In 1912, the Treaty of Fez established the French administration of Moroccan territory, with a portion of northern Morocco controlled by Spain and an international zone in and around Tangier.

Euphemistically designated as the 'protectorate', the French administration of Morocco was established after protracted and sometimes bloody military operations which finally achieved pacification of the territory in 1934. The Protectorate bureaucracy, under Marshal Lyautey, attempted with varying success to graft itself on to indigenous political hierarchies, undertook the construction of modern roads and railways, and sponsored agrarian reform and development. A growing contingent of French *colons* arrived in Morocco to become farmers or to live in the cities. French policy limited changes which would have caused great disruption in the existing ways of life of the Moroccan population, so they built new European quarters next to the existing *medinas* ('old towns') throughout the Protectorate.

Despite their reconstruction projects, the French did not succeed in buffering Morocco against the Great Depression (the Protectorate also had an exploitative aspect). French relations with the sultanate and with the Moroccan people became increasingly strained as Moroccans became more sensitive to European domination. In the 1940s, the nationalist movement gained momentum despite French efforts to curb its appeal. Spearheaded by Morocco's *Istiqlal* Party, demands for independence became more and more strident. Political demonstrations, some laced with skirmishes, confrontations and violence, occurred in the cities. The French allowed the sultanate an increasingly active part in their joint effort to quell grassroots agitation. But the Sultan was also a symbol of Moroccan identity and Islamic tradition, and so became a potent rhetorical element in the discourse of independence and in the propaganda against the French. They exiled him in 1953, first to Corsica, then to Madagascar. Two years later, he returned to the throne, and Moroccan independence was re-established in 1956.[1]

Neither the women of Marrakech nor Peets herself appear to have been immediately involved in this succession of political transformations. Yet however indirectly, Peets' stories show how they responded to them. The presence of a European population in Marrakech was certainly felt by these women despite the degree to which they seem to have been sequestered. They gradually altered their attitudes towards themselves, their husbands and families, and their sense of being Moroccan. The tone and tenor of their voices, like that of Peets herself, changed. The women appear to have come to a more overt awareness of their culture which at the same time became increasingly problematic in their own eyes. How they regard themselves and others and how they speak among themselves and to others about themselves became more critical, more self-reflective and possibly more ambiguous in relation to a formerly unquestioned tradition. Peets became intimately involved and invested in this unsettling and uncertain process. Her writing is an eloquent and elegant testament to these complex, intriguing but sometimes painful experiences.

Peets' voice is not Moroccan; her eloquence is distinct from that of indigenous storytellers such as Mrabet (1969, 1976, 1980) or Hamri (1975). Nor is she an expatriate novelist like Paul Bowles (1952, 1955) or John Hopkins (1972). Her voice also differs from that of a journalist writing of a whirlwind sojourn or of a longer period of residence (Kramer 1970). Peets is no anthropologist, though anthropologists may well envy the luxury of her lengthy stay. And she is not, at least overtly, feminist in her orientation, as is Moroccan sociologist Fatima Mernissi

---

1. For an introduction to the twentieth-century political history of Morocco, see Harris (1921), Ashford (1961), Cerych (1964), Barbour (1965), Bernard (1968), Geertz (1968), Waterbury (1970), Scham (1970), Burke (1976), Laroui (1977), and Hoisington (1984).

(1975, 1977). Her voice is quite simply that of a writer who is not out to present herself in a particular role, but instead to describe, render and perhaps dramatise the lives of women in Marrakech from the standpoint of an inside outsider.[2] Within the broader context outlined already, her 'ethnographic fictions', which appear here in English for the first time, are a significant addition to the large, diverse and growing corpus of writing on Muslim women (see Bibliography).

Marrakech has long been a source of mythological references, one element in a system of symbols through which Europeans have formed their conception of the Other. The Marrakech of the women about whom Peets writes is not that of the *souks* (markets), the palaces or mosques, or of the *ville nouvelle* (European quarter) but the Marrakech of rooftop afternoons, nights at the baths (*hammam*), marriage arrangements, household affairs, illness, visits to local saints' shrines, jealousy and witchcraft, camaraderie and mutual support, magic and suspicion, family life, childrearing and childbearing, encounters with neighbours, and problems with co-wives, sisters, mothers and friends. The management of households and husbands is another ubiquitous preoccupation. Peets depicts women's lives largely as family life *per se*. Since that is the heart of social life in so many societies, this particular feminine vantage-point provides an essential view of Marrakech life. The apparent insularity or perhaps, from the European point of view, the claustrophobia of women's lives in Marrakech during the period — as well as that of the windowless houses and labyrinthine alleyways of the *medina* which enclose them — do not, however, allow the interpretation that women's experience is only tenuously linked to the wider, heterogeneous social life of Marrakech as a complex urban space.

Although the exact date of the city's foundation is uncertain, Deverdun (1959) traces it to the eleventh century AD. Marrakech began as a military camp and perhaps as a market established by the Almoravids, an early imperial dynasty of Saharan origin. The early growth of the city corresponds to the rapid ascent of the Almoravids who found the location to have strategic value in controlling the surrounding region. The city developed as the Almoravids extended their

2. Life-history materials about Moroccan men and their experiences with colonialism and European modernism are plentiful. Recent anthropological accounts include Waterbury (1972), Crapanzano (1980), Dwyer (1982), Munson (1984) and Eickelman (1985). Autobiographical accounts in English include Charaibi (1955), Choukri (1973) and Charhadi (n.d.).

power northward and as trade routes, connecting Spain, northern Morocco and the Sahara, were regularised. By the early twelfth century, a large-scale system of *khettara*, a subterranean network of conduits and cisterns, had been constructed, thus laying the groundwork for urban expansion. The Almoravids also endowed the city with mosques, palaces, gardens and *fondouks* or caravansarais.

During the hegemony of the Almohad dynasty, beginning in the twelfth century, the city began to attract scholars, poets and theologians. The Merinids of the thirteenth and fourteenth centuries neglected the city, their empire centering to the north in Fez. Marrakech again became an imperial centre with the establishment of the Saadian dynasty in the fifteenth century. The Saadians built the El Badi palace, 'the incomparable', the vast ruins of which are today the setting for Morocco's annual folklore festival. Few modern tourists in Marrakech miss the Saadian tombs, a complex of intricately decorated structures featuring stone and tile filigrees, inlays and mosaics.

The still reigning Alaouite dynasty began in the seventeenth century to restore many of the city's long-neglected mosques and sanctuaries. The original *casbah* (citadel), royal palace and mosque of Marrakech have all disappeared. But the monumental Koutoubia mosque and minaret, built early in the city's history, still remain, together with an extensive system of bulky medieval fortifications — the famous red walls, bastions and gateways of the city — and a scattering of saints' tombs, residential quarters (including a separately walled *mellah* or Jewish quarter) and extensive *souks*.[3]

The construction of the *ville nouvelle* during the Protectorate period marked a dramatic shift in the overall ecology and demography of the city. This quarter, to the north and west of the *medina*, was laid out along wide avenues and boulevards, following contemporary French notions of urban design, and in stark contrast to the older neighbourhoods of the city. Business establishments and large apartment buildings were distributed along the main streets. Residential areas consisted of blocks of villas widely spaced within private gardens, often with walls and gateways protecting them from the street. While the majority of the European population lived in the familiar environment of the *ville nouvelle*, the symbiosis of this segment of the city with the older ones was lively, and the interchange between them brisk. Perhaps it was a

---

3. For a provocative analysis of the *souk* as an institution in Moroccan society, see the essay by Clifford Geertz in *Meaning and Order in Moroccan Society* (1979).

haven for Europeans, but it certainly served as a showcase of European modernism and city life for the Moroccans, who were as sensitive to its drawbacks as they were drawn to its attractions and anonymity.

In sum, the pre-colonial city owed its existence and development to favourable strategic and geographical factors, plentiful water, and the episodic attentions of the *makhzen* (government), which invested extensively in the city over the centuries. Marrakech also became a market and artisan centre, a caravan crossroads on the threshold of the Sahara, and a pilgrimage destination. A population of French *colons*, a colonial administration, a new railway and road links with the rest of Morocco added other dimensions to an already complex urban milieu. The cumulative effects of the city's variegated history is not a blend but an orchestrated diversity of Berber, Islamic and European elements.[4]

Approached from the north or west, the city itself is heralded by grand palm groves which stretch in broad belts about its walled perimeter. In stark contrast to the arid Haouz plain, there is a profusion of parks and gardens within the city. Olive, lime, pomegranate, orange and almond trees abound, and pastel festoons of flowering bougainvillea tumble over the garden walls. The bus from Casablanca sets its passengers down at one side of Djemma el-Fna, the city's great square. From the square, the Koutoubia mosque and adjacent citrus groves dominate the prospect, a theatrical backdrop for the life of the city. The Koutoubia's excessively tall, ancient and elaborately designed minaret is the hub about which the dance-like activities of the city's inhabitants seem to revolve. Djema el-Fna is an irregularly shaped open space surrounded by cafés, mosques and numerous merchant stalls. In the early morning it is only sparsely populated, but after the mid-day heat it gradually becomes crowded. By evening, it is teeming with people who have come to consult fortune-tellers and to watch midgets, acrobats, snake charmers, jugglers, magicians and story-tellers. There are sleight-

---

4. Fernea's (1975:217–8) imaginative delineation of the structure of Marrakech as an urban space captures the political and historical themes that are relevant to understanding it:

I began to envision the city of Marrakech as a giant and fanciful tree. If one thought of Gueliz, the modern, western part of the city, as a trimmed and shaped topiary tree, such as one finds in the gardens of Versailles, then Boulevard Mohammed Cinq was the trunk of the trees. And at the end of the trunk lay the roots, the thousands of tiny, tendril-shaped streets and alleys . . . that converge in some fashion of natural growth rather than imposed designs upon larger tendrils, which emerged at the last into the trunk again, nourishing, invisibly, the artificial topiary growth beyond.

of-hand artists and holy men each of whom attracts a ring of spectators. The square is an eternal circus and provides plentiful material for reinforcing the orientalist prejudices of European tourists and journalists.

From the square one enters the *medina* and the *souks*, a medieval world which has probably changed little since the caravans began crossing the desert. During business hours, the *souks* are a tumultuous jumble of shoppers, merchants and workers. The shaded walkways reveal one colourful scene after another, and pungent or spicy scents accompany the view. The *souks* are loosely organised by trade, with the rug merchants in one area, brass dealers or cloth-sellers in another. Each speciality is concentrated in its own lane, compound or plaza. There is a lane of spice merchants and another of apothecaries. Here too are silversmiths and beadsellers with their colourful glass and amber jewellery. The activities of the *souk* are ostentatiously displayed along with what is for sale. Bartering is conducted histrionically within earshot of other potential customers and neighbouring merchants alike. Embroidered wedding slippers, *caftans* shot through with gold thread and ceramics glazed with brilliant geometric designs crowd in upon the thoroughfares. In contrast to the reticence with which the mosques, women and family life are regarded, the social activities of the *souks* are displayed with seductive immediacy (Canetti 1978: 19–20).

In the residential quarters of the *medina*, the lanes are quieter, and the houses present a mute, windowless, embattled façade to the pedestrian. Passing through the imposing keyhole gateways of the city's fortifications, there are further barriers. The locked doors of the houses are not there merely to prevent wandering eyes from viewing the women within, since similar barriers occur elsewhere. Mosque entrances are likewise carefully screened. An aerial view of these residential quarters reveals a modular succession of square rooftops fenestrated by the houses' central courtyards. The *medina* as a whole is a series of compounds within compounds, a layered network of enclosures and branches. Numerous secondary lanes and alleys branch from the larger arteries or lead into *cul de sacs* which allow entry into private dwellings, courtyards and domestic compounds. Historically, not only were the main gates of the city locked at nightfall, but these local neighbourhoods were also closed off, so that security was enforced at the city walls, and reiterated by the architecture of the units and sub-units within it.

Many alleyways or dead-end streets were and are residences of large familial groups which collectively own whole streets or neighbourhoods. The foreigner ambling down these alleys may be confronted by

apparent dead-ends, boisterous children or stern-faced women who prevent the intruder from entering private areas. From a main artery or
secondary street, one may catch a glimpse of a family courtyard shaded
by grape arbours in which an old man leans against a wall smoking, sun-
ning himself, or watching the children while the women sit together
preparing *couscous*. The *medina* is thus a whole series of gateways in
sociological as well as an architectural sense. Through these gateways,
access to groups and locales is regulated, interaction limited and controlled, and entry scheduled and manipulated.

Leonora Peets found the key that gave entry to this world of Marrakech
in the episodes of illness which her husband came to treat. Because of the
proscriptions regulating interaction between men and women, she must
have been an important part of her husband's work when illness struck the
women of the households. These encounters provided contacts which
Peets parlayed into deeper friendships that were enriched and made more
complex by the cultural differences. Her descriptions of these encounters
offer incisive vignettes of Moroccan lives and comprise a record of Peets'
own perceptions which is a contribution in itself.

European visitors to Marrakech are often advised by Moroccan companions not to look inquisitively across the rooftops or into the courtyards of
neighbouring houses. Etiquette makes it indelicate to pay too close attention to the affairs of one's neighbours' women. The rooftops, like the
houses, are the domain of women, and men make a particular point of
avoiding these areas. This proscription is a microcosm of the broader
patterns of Moroccan custom regarding male-female dynamics. It is an
emotionally charged social pattern for Moroccans and other Muslim
peoples and one which Europeans unfamiliar with these cultures often
find puzzling. For both of these reasons, much has been written about
women and male-female relations in this region.[5] Peets' stories stand at
the intersection of various categories of this literature.[6]

5. An introduction to this literature and its associated themes and issues can be found in
   Accad (1978*a*). Johnson-Davies (1976) is a skillfully selected anthology of short
   stories translated from Arabic, including several by women writers. Also see Beck
   and Keddie (1978), Fernea and Bezirgan (1977) and Fernea (1985).
6. A striking portrayal of a European man's encounter with the people of Marrakech by
   Mayne (1953) tells us little about the lives of women. This deficit, typical in accounts
   by men, may derive partly from the constraints on men interacting with women
   except within narrowly-defined contexts. As one might expect, the best writing on
   Moroccan women is by women. For an exception, see Bowles (1981), a chilling and
   poignant narrative of a Moroccan woman's gradual movement away from Moroccan
   culture; Chraibi (1972) is a humorous and moving account of a similar transition.

Mernissi's study (1975) argues that the oppression of women is the major theme in Moroccan inter-sex relations (cf. Sabbah 1984). Daisy Dwyer's (1978:166) ethnographic study documents the more general premise that, as in Marrakech, the lives of Moroccan women are quite separate from those of the men (see also Rosen 1978:562–3). Mernissi situates oppression and domination in terms of male sexual ideology which understands the bio-social power of women — their sexuality and their power to give birth to children — as a source of great danger and as a potential cause of social disorder (*fitna*). The strictures, prohibitions on and sequestering of women is seen as an effort on the part of men to keep the powers of women 'within bounds'. Peets tells of men's fears of women in 'Woman's Cunning'. Women's use of witchcraft and their manoeuvring 'behind the scenes' feed the fears of men, and Mernissi (1977) interprets these phenomena, together with women's pilgrimages to the shrines of saints, as women's attempts to create a social life for themselves in spite of male dominance and paranoia.[7] Rather than emphasising oppression, Davis (1978, 1984) stresses the power which women achieve in working with, through and around the many prohibitions encompassing their daily lives. As 'Woman's Cunning' suggests, men sometimes feel dominated by women's power, just as they dominate women.

Anthropological treatments of sex roles and male-female dynamics have worried over the degree to which male ideology dominates female ideology and the degree to which ideology dominates social practice. Peets' writing touches on these issues, not by adding to the clutter of scholarly theorising but by bringing the reader palpably into contact with Moroccan women's experience of the male-female separation. She does not delineate ideology *per se*, but exposes the ideas of women about power and the limits and possibilities for gaining power over their own lives in the context of particular events, incidents and situations. Peets' women are frequently unhappy or angry with their men. But they are not ideologues. They may not always go to the lengths of Tammou in Peets' 'Couscous of the Dead', but they are fundamentally women of action.

The difference between how men and women conceptualise their social realities in Morocco makes the implementation of a commonly

7. Rabinow (1975) and Crapanzano (1980:75–87) have both written incisively on the importance of domination in the analysis of Moroccan social formations and processes.

understood ethos and etiquette problematical. This rift between diver-
gent world-views and a largely shared ethos and morality is what the
women in Peets' stories are struggling with. The narratives which Peets
articulates display a process of bargaining for or negotiating a reality in
order to accommodate the rift (Rosen 1984). But this process is a far cry
from dialogue, since it does not open up a channel of direct communi-
cation with men. It is instead a strategic, innovative, discursive process
among women which Peets inspects in her stories. As in her novella-
length 'Elimination from the Harem', they display in meticulous detail
the forms and contours of power and knowledge which are locally mani-
fested in women's lives in this 'capillary region' of Moroccan society
where domination produces its most visible effects (Foucault 1980:39).

Oppression is not an attribute of Moroccan social structure *per se*, but
an experience and hence an issue within it. The women in Peets' stories
gradually become more explicit about this omnipresent theme. Peets is
no ideologue, and the significance of her stories is not ideological but
illustrative. They shed light on women's perceptions of their social experience and on their assertion of power within their own world and that
of their husbands, sons and brothers.

Oppression and power operate in the European discourse on
Moroccan male-female dynamics as a means of translating into terms
comprehensible to European sensibilities what is, for Moroccan women,
the 'work of interpretation'. In Peets' writing, this work is pictured as
imaginative symbolic realignments and ceaseless re-articulations, often
competitive and acrimonious, of social statuses and roles. Women
attempt to make relationships more meaningful, durable and tolerable.
But as Peets shows, their success in these efforts is limited. In subsequent
writing on the problems of Moroccan women, this site of meaning-
making becomes the site of political struggle.

The work of women anthropologists on Moroccan women confirms
these interpretations while concentrating largely on rural women (Davis
1977, 1978, 1984, Dwyer 1978, 1978a, Maher 1974, 1978). Hildred
Geertz (1979) is a transitional case, since she studied family life in a larger
town, but studies of urban women are notably scarce. Rural women are
generally more apt to be involved in some aspects of agricultural labour,
whereas urban women, and particularly those of the middle and upper
classes, appear to have a more restrained and restricted style of
life.

One of my Moroccan informants suggested that because of the
necessities of rural living, rural women may have a broader context in

which to seek and to exercise power than is the case for urban women. On the other hand, urban women have been closer to modern European influences. For this reason, urban women have been the ones to become the most vehement in their protests against women's place in Moroccan society. Perhaps they have viewed their lives as more restricted than those of rural women. Upper-class women may not have had to rely on physical movement outside their homes in order to carry on complex social relations independent of their men. Although in Peets' time women had available various emissaries, message-carriers and net-working devices, the increasing use of the telephone more recently has greatly facilitated this pattern. Even so, urban women were and are restricted, although the particulars of just how they avoid restrictions have changed and perhaps become more variable than in Peets' day.

In general, it is urban women who have had better access to literacy and who have begun to demand change and to seek employment on their own. They have written the novels and stories of struggle and protest (Accad 1978). The voices of rural women have come to us largely through anthropologists, whereas urban women in North Africa have increasingly spoken for themselves through their fiction.[8] Peets' authen-tication of women's halting and gradually emerging self-awareness between 1930 and 1970 prefigures both the anthropological exposé of women's dealings with domination, biculturalism, change, even careerism and national identity, and the rendering of these themes in the francophone literature of urban, largely middle-class North African writers, many of whom have pursued their work by emi-grating to France (see Ben Jelloun 1973, 1978, 1983, Rabinow 1978, El Saadoui 1980, Fernea 1985).

Peets' stories resonate sympathetically with the emerging concerns of both anthropologists and indigenous writers and novelists. They antici-pate the recent work in both areas by touching upon many facets of change and struggle experienced by Moroccan women. In her early 'Apparitions', women devise means of circumventing customary rules limiting their movement outside the home in order to satisfy their

---

8. For an overview of this literature, see Accad (1978) and Nisbet (1984). N'Ait Attik (1974) is an important additional testament of her experience by a Moroccan woman of rural origins, but she is only able to speak to us by means of European interven-tion, translation and appropriation (of course, this point also applies to Peets' stories). Davis (1977) is another example of this kind of text. For perspectives from literature on urban women, see El Saadoui (1980) and Rifaat (1983).

curiosity about how Europeans live and what their homes are like. Their subversion of traditional strictures may itself be a traditional coping strategy which they use here to learn about cultural difference.

Peets' commentary on Marrakech custom continues in 'The Seventh Wife', in which a young woman's naiveté is shattered all too precipitately by marriage and sudden divorce from a man who shows little concern for her desires or her family's honour. In this story there is not only the problem of a 'scatterbrained' husband, as the young woman's irate father calls him, but of the position of women in relation to masculine power and ideology. The young woman's function as a token in a social exchange is enhanced not only by the arbitrary exercise of male prerogative, regardless of her wishes: Fadila's ignorance of the implications and expectations of marriage allows her to be intimidated and overwhelmed; her desires are made irrelevant by this ignorance. Only after the marriage breaks up is she able to be clear about her preferences, and by then it is too late. She decides that she wants her husband back, only to have to come to terms with his untimely death.

Peets ends this story by chiding Fadila for her sorrow. Because she is so young, she is certain to have another chance. This little tragedy is not simply a matter of its 'having been written'; it also shows how women's lives become submerged by the tumultuous demands made upon them by masculine priorities. As the women in Fadila's family cast about to identify a contingency to account for the unhappy turn of events, cultural difference also becomes grist for their mill. Peets had been invited to attend Fadila's wedding. The bride was held high on a brass tray and carried out to join her husband, but one of the women holding the tray tripped just as she stepped close to Peets' position in the audience. The moral of the story, which conforms perfectly with Moroccan convention, is that it is a mistake to invite a Christian to a wedding. Because Christians do not observe the commands of Islam, they can do nothing to assuage the untrustworthy spirits which may be dangerous to the bride.

'Mourning the Court Councillor' tells of the problematic inheritance of the widow of a wealthy and influential man. In this story, Peets lays out the mosaic of pathos and ritual which regulates mourning and the departure of the deceased. The ordering of the dead man's household according to custom creates a stately and subdued atmosphere in which the grief of the wife and family are expressed. There are the fresh matting and the candle at the head of the corpse, the green shroud to indicate that the dead man was a descendant of the Prophet, and the members of the religious brotherhood who come to chant. Peets' terse, vivid descriptions of each component of the setting and the procedures have a vivid immediacy. It appears that legally the widow inherits only one-eighth of her husband's estate because she is childless, but her husband declared on his deathbed that the house and everything in it would go to his widow, thus conferring considerable wealth upon her. The strictures of the law are bent to accommodate commitment, affection and respect. Yet from this angle too, the dependence of the woman upon the decisions of the man is dramatically demonstrated; things could have gone the other way. But the widow has her house and, as tradition dictates, her brother-in-law will become her new companion in life, once she has observed the obligatory four months of mourning. This extraordinary portrayal shows Peets at the height of her powers as she conveys the quality of life mandated for women as their situation is shaped by circumstance and by the exigencies of their culture.

Peets strikes a lighter note in 'Nevermore', a comedy of an affectionate husband and wife thrown against each other by male preoccupations with masculine domination. In the end, they are reunited by their clever side-stepping of the laws regulating divorce and remarriage. Peets shows how aspects of Morocco's legal system go against the grain of the up-and-down sociability that sometimes results from the ambivalence between the sexes. It is also clear in this story, as in 'Mourning the Court Councillor', that the legal system can be manipulated to one's advantage. The uncertain and repeated encounter with cultural difference as women experience it is discussed in many of the stories and is given anecdotal attention whenever Peets includes herself in the narrative. In 'Fatherly Love', European attitudes to womanhood, disease, fatherly responsibility and etiquette are shown at cross-purposes with comparable Moroccan attitudes.

In 'The Baths' Peets tells of going to the *hammam* with the women of the *cadi's* (judge) family. It is a cold November night, and the women wait in the draughty courtyard while the men are inside. When the women's turn finally comes, they pass the inferno-like furnace where shadowy figures stoke the fire with dry palm leaves. They then pass through vaulted halls and corridors lit by guttering lamps which provide an inadequate, wavering light. Here Peets is initiated into bathing, Moroccan style. The proceedings have already taken on an aura of ritual, and Peets seems to be penetrating a cultural inner sanctum.

She quickly rationalises her initial mystification when her companions reject her Estonian soap and sponge. She looks for similarities between the *hammam* and the Estonian sauna. She has the soles of her feet massaged with a rough stone. Her hair is shampooed with finely ground clay. The dim light preserves the privacy of each bather. The dry heat lulls everyone into a delightful torpor. Soon the men knock loudly on the door, bidding the women hurry. Peets emerges refreshed. She acknowledges her good fortune in being able to visit the baths where non-Muslims are rarely admitted. But she has been chastened by the women's lack of interest in her own bathing customs. And she has been cautioned about the malevolent spirits which inhabit such places: the *cadi's* secretary tells a ghost story about the baths which he himself experienced.

'Elimination from the Harem', perhaps the centrepiece of the collection, is a *tour de force* of ethnography, intrigue and storytelling skill which makes transparent some of the real-life consequences of Moroccan tradition. It explodes European stereotypes and further documents the complexities of family life in Marrakech during the period. In fact, Peets begins the story with an explicit discussion of the 'connotation of Oriental glamour' which the *harem* evokes for the European; because non-Muslims could not enter the *harem*, it became a perfect site for fantasising about Islamic culture. Many of the story's early passages are devoted to de-mystifying the *harem* by showing how it worked in practice as 'the living space a Muslim man allocates to his wife or wives'. Peets' description is not so much prosaic as meticulously detailed, so that the Moroccan version of this institution can be easily visualised.

The household of Hadj Kadur, who has three wives, is Peets' case-study. She describes their daily lives, their mutual suspicions and jealousies, and the final excommunication of one of them after she has used witchcraft to try to make the Hadj impotent with all women but herself. Peets delineates, with much richness of detail, how these women live together. Not having children to occupy their energies, the co-wives worry over their clothing and jewellery, the meals and rituals of the religious holidays, and the small gestures and innuendoes which create an atmosphere of controlled conflict. The scene changes abruptly once the Hadj discovers and aborts Keltoum's witchcraft, and children are adopted to grace the household. The remaining co-wives clearly continue to be dissatisfied with their lot and jealous of each other, despite their husband's efforts to provide for every want and vanity. The chronic structural realities of the *harem* and polygyny persist: split loyalties, the attendant suspicions and petty rivalries which preclude amicability and solidarity among the women.

In 'An ex-Christian's Sick Visit' crossing cultural boundaries appears in a rather arduous guise: a Christian woman convert to Islam finds that her acceptance as a Muslim by other women remains at best partial and fraught with suspicion. 'The First Additional Wife' returns to the impact of marriage customs on women as a gathering of friends for afternoon tea turns into an occasion for recounting their agonising experiences of admitting a co-wife into their husband's household.

With the final story, a halting yet compelling evolutionary trajectory has become evident: in 'Such a Custom Must be Abolished', a traditionally socialised Moroccan woman finally voices her emotionally charged protest against female submission. Her sardonic repudiation tells of a long history of anger and bitterness. The veiled protests of the women in Peets' earlier stories are at last manifest. There are formidable affinities and convergences here — if not exact concordances — between Peets' writing and recent anthropological analyses of Moroccan male-female dynamics and the interpretations of North African writers.

Women's skill in magic and their use of magical procedures in particular situations is a frequent topic in Peets' stories. One would be tempted to explain the recurrence of this theme in terms of her involvement in medicine and illness. Along with visits to saints' tombs, magical knowledge and practice in Morocco is a means of treating illness and misfortune (Foster 1985). Under certain circumstances, magic is an alternative to Western medicine. The relative merits and drawbacks of Moroccan and Western practices were no doubt a frequent topic of discussion and debate at the clinic of Dr Peets, the author's husband, and in the households which he visited. The importance of magic and its intimate connection with curing is also suggested by the complex pharmacopoeia available in the *souks* from the apothecaries' stalls.

But magic has a broader meaning than is suggested by its use as medicine. In both 'Couscous of the Dead' and 'Elimination from the Harem', it is given a central role in the ways used by women to attempt to regulate the behaviour of men to their own advantage. (Perhaps the reason why women resort to witchcraft is that they have little recourse in a legal system built around the legitimacy of masculine hegemony.) It is noteworthy that in both of these cases, the magic backfires, causing harm to the practitioner rather than to the intended victims. Thus, magic demonstrates its overweening power and resulting danger; it must be used with exquisite care and cunning, particularly when it is an accoutrement of conflict. Magic is not used destructively only against men as is evident in the conflicts between co-wives.[9] For the women of Marrakech, the significance of magic, whether used for good or ill, must be understood in broadly social and cultural terms; magic is a major idiom or 'technology' of social power. By means of their magical knowledge, they attempt to counter the social power of men, to promote health and comfort for themselves, and to increase their own power over social and biological processes alike. In her portrayals of magic, Peets describes a set of practices which appeals to the more lurid stereotypes that Westerners have of Islamic culture.

In provoking thought on the issue of women's power and submission in Morocco, Peets' stories also address the theme of change in colonial Marrakech and since. Social and cultural change appears not to have followed any uni-directional pathway despite significant explication by women of their situation. Peets forcefully conveys the complexity of change in a city such as Marrakech. In this case, change is an emerging recognition that conditions are unsatisfactory. But that realisation does not lead women simply to adopt European attitudes or practices, since these too are questioned. In their critique of the colonial experience, there is change. Notions that formerly had a 'law-of-life' aspect are put in doubt. Women's questioning is itself a moment, a form and a source of change. They gradually recognise themselves as subject not only to men but to Europe. They raise questions about their culture, the social ideology of their men and the rationale for the way their own social situation has come about. They come to the point of initiating a semiotics of their society which is nevertheless closely tied to their everyday lives. This questioning leads in turn to a ceaseless decipherment, reformulation and experimentation which further tests the limits of their situation.

Fernea's (1975) lengthy narrative of her residence in Marrakech (1971–2) suggests that, whatever else has changed for women in this society, they remain culturally remote from the European woman who attempts to understand them. Although they became increasingly sympathetic with Fernea as her residence continued, the separation between the European and Moroccan women remained a gulf, something inherited which could not be altered. This stunning reality persists in spite of Fernea's knowledge of Arabic with all the symbolic advantages which

9. In Tangier, gossip had it that the magic which a Berber maid buried in a flower pot in her apartment made Jane Bowles lose her mind.

accrue to her because of it. Bringing into the foreground the story of her family's adjustment to Marrakech society, she fails where Peets succeeds in thoroughly rendering the subjective attitudes of the women she writes about. Perhaps inevitably, Fernea is able to give only surface dialogues, thus dramatising the cultural boundaries. These difficulties are handled sensitively and subtly in Peets' stories, since her relations with the women of Marrakech have gone considerably further than Fernea's.

An anecdote from Fernea's book (1975:34) explains in part women's resistance to Europeanisation, although they are also often enticed by it. It suggests also why Peets' women seek to redefine themselves and their style of life largely in Moroccan terms despite the freedom which westernisation may seem to promise:

'The French run things, especially the schools. They won't let Americans in the Lycée.'
'But Morocco is independent,' I protested.
Our landlady laughed.
Aisha laughed.
'Oh, yes, we are independent,' said Aisha, 'but the French still run everything.'[10]

Besides the historical antecedents of women's resistance to change in the guise of westernisation, the potency of Europe's Judeo-Christian tradition, in contradistinction to Islam, must also be acknowledged. If change is sought by women in Marrakech, it is not to be found in emulation and assimilation of European culture. In Peets' writing, there is little convergence of the culture of the women in Marrakech with that of their European counterparts. As in Fernea's book, Peets' women remain aloof from many aspects of European social ideology, instead becoming more articulate in expressing their hesitations, questions and resistances both to westernisation and to tradition. They may envy the kitchen of the European housewife; but they have reservations about European morality and styles of dress.

The question of change also raises the question of the possibility of the European relating to and comprehending the Other, since knowing the

10. The whole of this interpretation pertains solely to the women about whom Peets writes, not to Moroccan women in general. The responses on the part of Moroccan women to change and to European presence have been bewilderingly diverse, as the literature cited indicates. Some women have become relatively westernised and now feel more comfortable living outside Morocco, and many others would do so if they could. Fatima Zohra in Munson (1984) lives in the United States and is married to an American, but she has not repudiated her Moroccan or Muslim identity. North African women's response to change is a large topic which could only be given preliminary attention here.

Other is neither inevitable nor easily arranged by simple proximity. As represented by Peets' women, the Other remains other, although her writing allows a certain *rapprochement*. But cultural difference remains largely irreducible on the level of day-to-day social practice. There still remains a cultural barrier between Moroccan women and Westerners such as Peets or Fernea. It is a sort of 'demilitarised zone' or margin which constantly shifts its ground, operating both as an incitement to interaction and as an impediment.

Fernea has to struggle for the wary and provisional acceptance which she obtains from the neighbourhood women in the *medina*, whereas Peets appears largely to have succeeded in a similar struggle, becoming participant record-keeper. The cultural differences and idiosyncrasies still persist, subtly questioning the social discourse between Moroccan and European. Peets has a fine narrative style and a keen eye for critical incidents and details, and thus while difference remains, her skill both as a writer and in her way of comporting herself, does much to mediate and attenuate this insoluble difficulty.

On a first reading, many of the stories could be taken as representing the most 'orientalist' and exotic distortions of an earlier Western view of Islam. But it would be misleading to characterise Peets' choice of themes as orientalist, or her work as contributing to that discourse rather than questioning it. The terms and texture of orientalism as an histori- cally-derived form of discourse were already in place by the time Peets began working in Marrakech. An allusion to orientalism is inevitable because Peets' subject-matter is precisely that which was so often appro- priated by its practitioners.

Thinking of how to resist this well-established and highly-charged set of terms is daunting for, as Said (1978:96) suggests, 'orientalism over- rode the orient.' It overrides Peets' subject-matter too, setting up some unhappy and unwelcome distortions and impediments to 'description'. Orientalism is a form of discourse or 'knowledge', 'whose material presence or weight, not the originality of a given author, is really responsible for the texts produced out of it' (Said 1978:94). *Women of Marrakech* is a text which participates, however unwillingly, in this discursive 'situation'. To what extent does Peets' work resist or escape it? It resists orientalism by tacitly providing a sustained and subtle critique of European culture and the domination of men. It escapes it to the degree that it conveys feminine subjectivities in their own terms and struggles to uncover what is 'true' of these women's lives, since such truths are often revealed only with nuance and difficulty, given European preconceptions. Peets' stories are a dialogue with orientalism rather than just an uncritical repetition of its voyeuristic appropriation of what it defines as exotic. As 'ethnographic fictions', they come to terms with the Other, not by claiming to bridge the differences, but by showing that from the side of the European and from the side of the Moroccan, assimilating the Other will always be incomplete and distorted.

In fact, Peets' work appears at times to be rather hermetic, self-enclosed, as are the women's lives. The stories, for better or worse, avoid the encounter between the world of women and the 'outside' world and the political and historical exigencies of the times. The connection between the microcosm of women and the macrocosm of the public life of their husbands, of European occupation and of the changes that their children experienced outside the home, are present in the stories, but they are understated (cf. Chraibi 1972). Similarly, Peets is often, though not invariably, self-effacing. She tells us little about how she worked in relation to her husband's medical practice, where and how they lived. The reader is left to speculate on these matters.

Her eloquence puts the reader in touch with the sympathy and humour which she and the women she met brought to their relationships. She cleverly emphasises rapport rather than disjunction. The later stories are increasingly sophisticated, reflecting her greater familiarity with Moroccan society. Despite the cultural differences, Peets constitutes a compelling aesthetic of the lives of the women of Marrakech; her ethnographic veracity ironically acknowledges how different those lives are from her own, appreciating in them elements that are satisfying while others are anxiety-provoking and transitional.

Peets shows a mastery of narration and an attention to detail that engage the reader in a vivid experience of seeing and hearing the lives of Others. In 'The First Additional Wife' she makes her characters into ardent *raconteurs* of their experiences with co-wives; in 'Woman's Cunning' her narrators are two men who employ Moroccan traditional story-telling techniques to illustrate aspects of male sexual ideology; in 'Elimination from the Harem' and 'Couscous of the Dead' the narrative goes forward on a rising tide of conflict and suspense. Lyrical touches and vivid details relate the broad narrative sweep of the stories to their settings. The teeth of the handsome hero in 'Couscous of the Dead' are compared to 'chunks of sugar on the merchant's counter'. In the same story, Peets refers to her attempts to understand veiled references to witchcraft as finding the missing letter which solves a crossword puzzle. This imagery indeed indicates Peets' sharpness of observation; but her reference to crossword puzzles also reveals a canny ethnographer, explicating what people can only refer to indirectly.

Compelling narrative, incisive detail and lyrical imagery recur throughout, and are complemented by dialogue of an immediacy which permits a hard realism rarely evident in academic anthropological writing. These elements together have the cumulative effect of presenting 'ethnographic fiction' a singularly accessible medium. Such is Peets' hybrid achievement.

If the women of Marrakech still remain Other, if cultural difference persists in spite of ourselves, and our habits of appropriating and domesticating what is 'strange' — through colonialism or through writing — Peets' work belies this seemingly hopeless conundrum. The result of her mediations is not to create the compelling illusion that the Other is simple-mindedly ourselves. Instead, her experience and the web of veracity which she weaves in her writing points out the authenticity of an encounter which acknowledges and preserves difference. The otherness of the women of Marrakech, as Peets depicts it, becomes in these stories the self-justifying distinctiveness of a mode of being which haughtily holds itself apart from European domination. Women's power and knowledge in Morocco are in part maintained by this assertion of differences, and are promoted by their forceful representation in these stories.

Department of Anthropology
University of California, Berkeley

BIBLIOGRAPHY

Accad, Evelyn (1978), 'The Theme of Sexual Oppression in the North African Novel', in Lois Beck and Nikkie Keddie (eds), *Women in the Muslim World*, Cambridge, Mass.: Harvard University Press.

—(1987*a*), *Veil of Shame: The role of women in the contemporary fiction of North Africa and the Arab world*, Québec: Editions Naaman.

Ashford, Douglas E. (1961), *Political Change in Morocco*, Princeton, N.J.: Princeton University Press.

Barbour, Nevill (1965), *Morocco*, London: Thames and Hudson.

Beck, Lois, and Nikkie Keddie (eds) (1978), *Women in the Muslim World*, Cambridge, Mass.: Harvard University Press.

Ben Jelloun, Tahar (1973), *Harrouda*, Paris: Editions Denoël.

—(1977), *La plus haute des solitudes*, Paris: Editions du Seuil.

—(1983), *L'écrivain public*, Paris: Editions du Seuil.

Bernard, Stéphane (1968), *The Franco-Moroccan Conflict, 1943–56*, New Haven, Conn.: Yale University Press.

Bowles, Paul (1952), *Let It Come Down*, New York: Random House.

—(1955), *The Spider's House*, New York: Random House.

—(1981), 'Here to learn' in *Midnight Mass*, Santa Barbara, Calif.: Black Sparrow Press.

Burke, Edmund III (1976), *Prelude to Protectorate in Morocco*, Chicago: University of Chicago Press.

Canetti, Elias (1978), *The Voices of Marrakech* (J.A. Underwood, trans.), New York: Seabury.

Cerych, Ladislav (1964), *Européens et Marocains, 1930–1956*, Bruges: De Tempel.

Charhadi, Driss ben Hamed (1964), *A Life Full of Holes* (Paul Bowles, Trans.), London: Weidenfeld and Nicolson.

Choukri, Mohamed (1973), *For Bread Alone* (Paul Bowles, trans.), London: Peter Owen.

Chraibi, Driss (1955), *Les Bouches*, Paris: Editions Denoël.

—(1972), *La civilisation, ma mère!*, Paris: Editions Denoël.

Crapanzano, Vincent (1980), *Tuhami, Portrait of a Moroccan*, Chicago: University of Chicago Press.

Davis, Susan (1977), 'Zahra Muhammad, a Rural Woman of Morocco' in Elizabeth W. Fernea and Basima Q. Bezirgan (eds), *Middle Eastern Muslim Women Speak*, Austin: University of Texas Press.

—(1978), 'Working Women in a Moroccan Village', in Lois Beck and Nikkie Keddie (eds), *Women in the Muslim World*, Cambridge, Mass.: Harvard University Press.

—(1984), *Patience and Power*, Boston: Schenkman.

Deverdun, Gaston (1959), *Marrakech, dès origines à 1912* (2 vols), Rabat:

21

Editions Techniques Nord-Africaines.

Deihl, Gaston (1963), *Delacroix au Maroc*, Rabat: Mission Universitaire et Culturelle Française.

Dwyer, Daisy (1978), *Images and Self-images*, New York: Columbia University Press.

—(1978a), 'Women, Sufism and Decision-making in Moroccan Islam' in Lois Beck and Nikkie Keddie (eds), *Women in the Muslim World*, Cambridge, Mass.: Harvard University Press.

Dwyer, Kevin (1982), *Moroccan Dialogues: Anthropology in question*, Baltimore: Johns Hopkins University Press.

Eickelman, Dale (1985), *Knowledge and Power in Morocco: The education of a twentieth-century notable*, Princeton, N.J.: Princeton University Press.

El Saadoui, Nawal (1980), *The Hidden Face of Eve: Women in the Arab world* (Sherif Hetata, trans.), London: Zed Press.

Fernea, Elizabeth (1975), *A Street in Marrakech*, New York: Doubleday.

—(ed.) (1985), *Women and the Family in the Middle East*, Austin: University of Texas Press.

—and Basima Q. Bezirgan (eds) (1977), *Middle Eastern Muslim Women Speak*, Austin: University of Texas Press.

Foster, Stephen W. (1981), 'Interpretations of Interpretations', *Anthropology and Humanism Quarterly*, 6, 4, 2–8.

—(1982), 'The Exotic as a Symbolic System', *Dialectical Anthropology*, 7, 1, 21–30.

—(1984), 'Deconstructing a text on North Africa', *Pre/Text*, 4, 3–4, 295–315.

—(1985), 'Magic', *Anthropology and Humanism Quarterly*, 10, 3, 81.

Foucault, Michel (1980), *Power/Knowledge: Selected interviews and other writings, 1972–1977* (Colin Gordon, ed.), New York: Pantheon.

Gallagher, Charles F. (1963), *The United States and North Africa*, Cambridge, Mass.: Harvard University Press.

Geertz, Clifford (1968), *Islam Observed*, New Haven, Conn.: Yale University Press.

—(1979), 'Suq: The bazaar economy in Sefrou' in Clifford Geertz, Hildred Geertz and Lawrence Rosen, *Meaning and Order in Moroccan Society*, New York: Cambridge University Press.

Geertz, Hildred (1979), 'The Meaning of Family Ties' in Clifford Geertz, Hildred Geertz and Lawrence Rosen, *Meaning and Order in Moroccan Society*, New York: Cambridge University Press.

Hamri, Mohamed (1975), *Tales of Joujouka* (Blanca Nyland, trans.), Santa Barbara, Calif.: Capra Press.

Harris, Walter (1929), *Morocco That Was*, Oxford: Blackwell.

Hoisington, William A. (1984), *The Casablanca Connection: French colonial policy, 1936–1943*, Chapel Hill, N.C.: University of North Carolina Press.

Hopkins, John (1972), *Tangier Buzzless Flies*, New York: Atheneum.

Johnson-Davies, Denys (ed.) (1976), *Moslem Arabic Short Stories*, London: Heinemann.

Kramer, Jane (1971), *Honour to the Bride like the Pigeon that guards its Grain under the Clove Tree*, London: Collins.

Laroui, Abdellah (1977), *The History of the Maghrib*, Princeton, N.J.: Princeton University Press.

Loti, Pierre n.d., *Morocco* (W.P. Baines, trans.), New York: Frederick A. Stokes and Co.

Maher, Vanessa (1974), *Women and Property in Morocco*, New York: Cambridge University Press.

—(1978), 'Women and Social Change in Morocco' in Lois Beck and Nikki Keddie (eds.), *Women in the Muslim World*, Cambridge, Mass.: Harvard University Press.

Mayne, Peter (1953), *The Alleys of Marrakech*, Boston: Little, Brown.

Mernissi, Fatima (1975), *Beyond the Veil: Male-female dynamics in a modern Muslim society*, Cambridge, Mass.: Schenkman.

—(1977), 'Women, Saints and Sanctuaries', *Signs*, 3, 1, 101–12.

Mrabet, Mohammed (1969), *The Lemon* (Paul Bowles, trans.), New York: McGraw-Hill.

—(1976), *Look and Move On* (Paul Bowles, trans.), Santa Barbara, Calif.: Black Sparrow Press.

—(1980), *The Beach Café and the Voice* (Paul Bowles, trans.), Santa Barbara, Calif.: Black Sparrow Press.

Munson, Henry (ed.) (1984), *The House of Si Abd Allah*, New Haven, Conn.: Yale University Press.

n'Ait Attik, Mririda (1974), *Songs of Mririda, Courtesan of the High Atlas*, Greensboro, N.C.: Unicorn Press.

Nisbet, Anne-Marie (1984), 'The Literary Treatment of Women in the Maghrebian Novel in French' in Freda Hussain (ed.), *Muslim Women*, London: Croom Helm.

Rabinow, Paul (1975), *Symbolic Domination*, Chicago: University of Chicago Press.

—(1977), *Reflections on Fieldwork in Morocco*, Berkeley: University of California Press.

—(1978), 'Working in Paris', *Dialectical Anthropology*, 3, 4, 361–4.

Rifaat, Alifa (1983), *Distant View of a Minaret* (Denys Johnson-Davies, trans.), London: Quartet.

Rosen, Lawrence (1978), 'The Negotiation of Reality: Male-female relations in Sefrou, Morocco' in Lois Beck and Nikkie Keddie (eds.), *Women in the Muslim World*, Cambridge, Mass.: Harvard University Press.

Sabbah, Fatna A. (1984), *Woman in the Muslim Unconscious* (Mary Jo Lakeland, trans.), New York: Pergamon.

Said, Edward (1978), *Orientalism*, New York: Pantheon.

Scham, Alan (1970), *Lyautey in Morocco*, Berkeley: University of California Press.

Waterbury, John (1970), *The Commander of the Faithful*, London: Weidenfeld and Nicolson.

—(1972), *North for the Trade*, Berkeley: University of California Press.

Wharton, Edith (1920), *In Morocco*, New York: Scribner's.

Vinogradov, Amal Rassam (1974), 'French Colonialism as Reflected in the Male-Female Interaction in Morocco', *Transactions of the New York Academy of Sciences*, 36, 192–9.

APPARITIONS

(1930)

Night had slipped into the house. For a while it roamed around in the guise of twilight, rapidly blurring all objects. Then it quickly swallowed the room and the minaret-studded city outside.

It was raining. Between the rills that crisscross the window pane, I could see the dark opening of Djemaa el-Fna, soundless and abandoned. It usually teemed with humanity, resounded with drumbeats, and wrapped itself into the sultriness of sun and the smoke of burning oil. Now it gaped in the dark like a huge drained pool. The small stalls bordering the square were shut — no customers were expected while this rain continued. Only some sellers of mint still crouched in the middle of the square, sheltered by mats and tattered burlap. Acetylene gas flames flickered on their stands, casting wavering reflections on the puddles.

The falling rain made a soft murmur. A cat meowed plaintively. A beggar sheltered in a nearby wall niche and intoned a long-drawn-out verse of the Koran. His voice rose and fell eerily in the silence of the night. The verse was repeated with racking persistence, unceasing — as if the homeless man who uttered it had lost all sense of time and place. I tried to read by the light of a kerosene lamp, but the beggar's wail ground into my ear.

I made a sudden involuntary start. Thuds could be heard on the wooden stairs leading from the street to our flat, then as well the soft sound of heelless slippers touching the steps. Grabbing the lamp, I hurried into the hall.

'Who is it?'

A stack of bedsheets heaved itself up the stairs. On the lower steps further white and black figures pottered about, faces all covered. The first one finally reached me. 'A-ah!' The panting bundle of sheets sounded a sigh of relief, as if wishing to say 'Thank God!' Then more composedly: 'Peace be with you!' Where had I heard this voice before?

A henna-stained hand with a brownish pattern appeared from

25

under the sheet and energetically pulled the kerchief away from the face. I recognised the junior wife of the overseer of city mosques — a recently-wed young woman perennially kept under seven locks.

There was no time to recover from my astonishment before the next figure crawled up to my feet, all tangled up in her *haik*, the large sheet worn by women in public. This was the senior wife's daughter. Would the third bundle, still stuck on the stairs, be her sister? I went down, stretched out my hand, and pulled her up into the hall. And now three little monks were clambering up, the hoods of their wet burnouses drawn deeply down on the eyes — brothers of the two girls. However, I looked in vain for the adult male escort, without whom such ladies should not go into the street even in broad daylight, not to mention at this late hour.

The young wife bit her lip, and her restless glance wandered around:

'Is the *tbib* at home?'

No, the doctor, my husband, was not at home. A sigh of relief. Only when they were all seated in the living room did I realise how nervous the young woman was. Her beautiful face had red blotches, her luscious and rather large mouth twitched, and the anxiety in her eyes was enhanced by kohl, an antimony eyeliner. I kept wondering to myself about the unusual visit, the time chosen for it, and in particular the lack of an escort.

'Who escorted you here?'

'We came by ourselves.'

Sensing the need for further explanation, the young wife added with feigned casualness:

'Sidi Mustafa, my husband, went to Rabat, on business. I was alone, so I decided to come and see your European style of life.' As if pressed for time, she impatiently ordered: 'Show me around in your house.'

Why test her patience? I got up with the lamp: 'Come.' Eagerly poking about, the visitors followed. Silently they looked at every piece of furniture, timidly touching various objects with just a finger. We had barely entered the bedroom, when someone behind me emitted a shriek: the senior wife's elder daughter was recoiling with horror toward the door. Her outstretched finger pointed to something in front of us:

'What . . . what is *that*? How horrible! Allah help me!'

That turned out to be a chair over the back of which the *tbib* had left his coat spread out. I sympathised with the girl: for her a high-legged chair was exotic enough, but superimpose on it a garb with pipelike sleeves, and it became really sinister.

'Holy prophet! What ghastly gadgets you keep around,' the girl grumbled. 'Crouching like an *afarit*, a head spirit! I am really scared to move around in your house.'

To calm their excited mood, I took them to the kitchen. This room was tiny, compared to the vast cooking section of the overseer's house. Yet it had one special attraction: a tap, which at a single turn spouted all the water one could wish. Such an innovation might well meet with the disapproval of the members of the Marrakech guild of water-carriers, who draw the vital fluid from city wells and take it to the households in goatskin pouches, but my visitors liked the idea. They fooled around with the jet of water, laughing and taking turns rinsing their hands. The young wife's amazement reached a climax when we reached the lavatory. She pulled the handle of the cistern eagerly and repeatedly, not wanting to leave such an interesting place.

On our return to the living room everyone was feeling cheerful. The young matron, in particular, had become sunny and talkative. Yes, everything was great in this European-style house. It was very pleasant to be on such a visit. Moreover, what a funny experience they had on their way! Laughing gave her hiccups, as she talked about it.

'There are many houses here side-by-side, and I didn't know which was yours. I tried the house next-door, and an unknown woman met me, and said she was the dentist. I shouted: no, no, it's not you I want; and keeping her away with my arms, I ran away. What a lark!' They all bent double with laughter.

'It's too bad that you came in the dark. In daylight the whole Djemaa el-Fna and half the city can be seen from my window. Next time, come during the day.'

The young wife's mood darkened at once: 'I can't come then.'

'But you did come today. What would hinder you from doing it again?'

'Today Sidi Mustafa was away.' She continued emphatically: 'Oh, it is so boring. Nowhere else to go but inside the house or on the roof terrace. House or roof, roof or house . . .'

'So your husband does not even know that you came here.'

'No.'

'Would he allow you to come?'

'No.'

'Not even in daylight?'

'No.'

The favourite wife of the supervisor of the mosques pierced the floor with her defiant glance and muttered through clenched teeth: 'But I came, never mind the consequences!'

Anxiety overwhelmed the room. The senior wife's elder daughter shifted on her chair, looked at me pleadingly, and her voice trembled:

'You won't tell father of our visit, will you?'

I promised to be as silent as the grave, and she said 'Baraka-laoufik! Thank you.'

This gratitude seemed so deeply felt that I began to appreciate the seriousness of the situation even more clearly. The spouse of a highly-placed husband had arbitrarily left her home at night, enticing with her the co-wife's daughters and sons — something unheard-of and shameful . . .

'But Lalla Rahalia?' I cautiously diverted the conversation to the senior co-wife. 'Did she not wish to come with you?'

There was a sly smile on the young wife's lips.

'Sidi Mustafa took Lalla Rahalia to the countryside, a week ago. A message had come that her father was dying.'

Even death sometimes came at just the right moment. . . .

'But won't the servants give the show away?' I pressed on.

She made a disdainful pout.

'Do you imagine they're not afraid of the whip? Besides, I told them we were going to pray at the tomb of Abdelaziz the saint. Once we were in the street we got a taxi and rode to your neighbourhood; the boys knew the location. To be on the safe side, we walked the last part of the journey. I had this clever plan figured out a long time ago! The rain was a special stroke of luck: there's no one in the streets.'

'So you will not even go to the saint's tomb?'

'We will drop in on our way back.' The lady lowered her voice, as if afraid of being disrespectful to the saint, something that could bring untoward consequences such as discovery of her escapade.

'Would your esteemed husband allow you to go to the mausoleum?'

'No.'

Even to pray, one had to go in secret, with the servants conniving. . . . What would the master say, if he heard about his wife's adventure? In my mind's eye the lean face of elderly Sidi Mustafa looked stern. . . . Suppose the boys suddenly dropped a few tell-tale words. . . . I turned towards them:

'Are you capable of keeping your mouth shut?'

It was a marvel how dead serious they could look. A nod affirmed that their lips would be sealed, come what may. I was present at a conspiracy. I was in a land where people know how to keep silent.

One of the boys held the handle of a brass kettle. What was this for?

'To take holy water back home, from the mausoleum. Quite a few of the servants have tooth-aches. Fadel, you haven't lost the candles, have you?'

The youngest boy fingered his fluffy burnous, and reassured the matron. Placing my hand on Fadel's stomach, I could indeed feel two thick sticks.

'What colour are the candles for the saint?' I asked. 'Are they plain or decorated?'

'One is green, and the other. . . .'

I will never know the colour of the other candle, because the boy stopped half-way through the word he was speaking. The apartment stairs were creaking under someone's steps. In a flash the boys pulled their hoods over their faces, and the women covered their heads with *haiks*. I knew those footsteps. Calm yourselves, my dear guests, the newcomer is none other than the *tbib*.

Tbib? The boys did not have to be afraid of him. They had seen him before, in their own home; they had even shaken hands with him. The doctor had also treated the leg wound of the younger daughter, but the overseer of mosques had not shown the *tbib* his elder daughter, not to mention his favourite wife.

Like grown-up men, the boys boldly let their hoods drop on to their shoulders. The younger girl's face reappeared more slowly, and her elder sister had let her face drop so low out of fright that she seemed in danger of falling off the chair.

The young matron's hands parted the protective sheet to either side of her face, wondering at the *tbib*. How was it that a male person could appear in the midst of women without asking permission? When the doctor held out his hand, a blush covered her face. But she accepted the hand greeting, and even dug the elder girl in the ribs, as if calling her to order. The smile on her lips showed that her composure had returned, and soon she even looked rather coquettish. As the conversation with the boys turned to the saint, the lady's energetic nature asserted itself. Authoritatively, though stammering slightly, she took command of the conversation:

'Oh, yes, the saint's grave is just at the place where the thick chain blocks the street. That chain prevents Jews and Christians from setting foot on hallowed ground. It isn't there for nothing. Once a French soldier crawled under the chain as a joke and do you know what happened? He dropped dead!'

'Isn't the lady afraid to move around in the streets at that late hour?' the *tbib* asked.

The young wife again wore the air of a cold-blooded gang leader. No, she was never afraid. She was able to read the Koran! Once when her husband was away, footsteps had been heard on the roof. Thieves, perhaps! She immediately seized a sheep-slaughtering knife and rushed to the rooftop, along with the boys. No one was there: maybe it had been the cats. Another time she spent half the night on the roof terrace, out of sheer boredom, watching the late passers-by. The next day she had a tremendous headache. 'That's what the night spirits did to you,' the others said, but she never saw a single spirit. Throwing her head back so

that her earrings and golden frontal adornment tinkled, she
declared:

'I am not afraid of the *djnun*, the spirits!'

'Say immediately: *besmellah rahman rahim* — in the name of the
gracious and merciful Allah!' The frightened girls raised their
arms in a warning gesture. 'Say it right away, if you don't want a
terrible mishap to strike us.'

'In the name of the gracious and merciful Allah,' the young
matron mumbled the formula for use against spirits, but quickly
and haughtily added, 'Still, I am not afraid of them.'

The impiety of their father's wife made the other members of
the family ill at ease. Silence reigned. The rain beat on the
window panes with renewed vigour. The young wife sat listening
to it, but all at once she stood up and commanded:

'This is a good time to leave. Let's go!'

They immediately started off, fumbling with their clothes.
Scarves were hurriedly knotted in front of their faces, the *haik*
corners heaped on top of their heads. May Allah's peace remain
with the *tbib*'s house!

After the crowd on the stairs, there was only silence outside the
house. Night and rain swallowed up the six conspirators.

The claws of the wind were grasping at the clicking window
frames. Rain rustled down. I suggested to myself that I had been
teased by apparitions, while all the time the favourite wife of the
overseer of the mosques was actually passing the evening at home
— in quiet and in prayer, her doors locked and bolted.

CHILDREN

(1935)

We sat cross-legged on the carpets spread out in the garden — four guests and Sidi Maati, the garden's owner. The place of honour naturally belonged to the eagle-faced *caid* Omar, still fiery-eyed but with his ox-like neck already bent by age, and his black beard sprinkled with white. His secretary sat next to him, an unassuming middle-aged man with a bloated white face. The *tbib* and I completed the group.

We formed a circle round a shiny brass tray with teapots and glasses, in the shade of a tall apricot tree. Water to irrigate the garden flowed cool and quiet in the shallow watering ditch nearby. The hot sun drew forth aromas from the mingled mint, clove, turnips and geraniums sown under the pomegranate trees around us.

Caid Omar leaned sideways on the cushion and turned his head, which was wrapped a cabbage-like turban. He asked the doctor in a half-whisper:

'*Tbib*, would you have any tonic medicine for me?'

He winked slyly at the *tbib*, as if to indicate that the question had a deeper meaning. I understood, and was not much surprised. Polygamy often produced a feeling of reduced virility among Moroccan men, especially the wealthier ones, and we often found that those in their fifties, but sometimes only in their thirties or even younger, turned to the doctor for advice and medicines, more often the latter. One might listen to sensible advice, but then to go and apply it to one's daily life was bothersome and unpleasant. *Caid* Omar, too, wanted some medicine. He would not be put off by a high price for the drugs, much less by their mode of application, even if that was injection. As an old warrior he was certain he could withstand even that. And he was absolutely convinced that such a medicine was known to the Nazarene (Christian) doctor from abroad. Oddly enough, the *tbib*'s answer missed the point, shifting attention to utterly trivial, unimportant side issues:

32

'How many wives do you have?'

The *caid* shrugged his shoulders: 'Three legal ones.' And added proudly: 'All of them white.'

'But how about concubines and . . . the blackskinned ones?' The *tbib* was on the point of saying 'slaves', but officially this category had been abolished, hadn't it?

'Ah, how about the negresses?' The *caid* burst out with a hearty laugh, drawing out the 'ee' sound. 'The negresses, you said? Should I have counted them? They come and go.'

The *caid* dismissed the matter with a gesture of his hand. What a funny question. Why keep track of anything so trivial. . . . Then Maati, the host, jumped to his feet with unexpected agility. Shaking the train of his several long robes, as if to rid himself of fleas, he shouted:

'See, that's how many women the *caid* has!'

At this buffoonery everyone gave a loud chuckle. The *caid*, flattered, graciously nodded assent.

'And how many children do you have?' the *tbib* inquired.

'Nine.'

'Is that all? With all those women?'

The *caid* threw back his head and after almost choking with laughter, he finally just managed to utter the words:

'Thirty . . . are . . . dead.'

I could not understand why the thought of thirty dead children could cause the father such mirth. Turning to the *caid*'s secretary, I asked how many children he had. He replied, 'Four.'

'And how many are dead?'

'Thirteen . . . I believe. . . .' This man's mouth was also turning up at the corners, and he was fighting off the temptation to laugh. It seemed that the *tbib* was a bit green. . . .

The physician brought his fist down on his knee: 'Damn it, what sort of a country is this? What's the point of your women going through childbirth so many times if you don't know how to raise your children to adulthood? Haven't I all too often seen, during my stay here, how you feed infants tea and oil? In winter, you cover yourselves with one woolen burnous on top of another, but as for the children, you roll their shirt trains up to their chests and have them crouch on stone floors with bare buttocks. Let me tell you, gentlemen, that out of every hundred infants in my country only a few die.'

'Is that so?' the men exclaimed as with one voice, their eyes open wide. But almost at once a smirk appeared on the *caid*'s face, and he observed jovially and a bit teasingly:

'Sure, after all, you have only one woman for every man. Hence the number of children is bound to be small, and this has scared you into learning how to take better care of them than we do. But look, *tbib*,' and the *caid* began to chuckle again: 'At home I have a whole legion of those women. If one started laying out their sleeping mattresses here, side by side, the line would reach this orange tree over there. And every single one of them absolutely wants to bear a child. Do you get the hang of it? Well, one tries to oblige as one can, and so those children come about. They are born, they perish, according to the design of the Almighty. It is not up to us. Allah gives, Allah takes.'

He continued in a more earnest vein: 'In this world parents receive children on loan only. When Allah wants to have his loan returned — blessed be his name. Still, some children do reach adulthood. . . .'

THE COUSCOUS OF THE DEAD

(1938)

When we settled in Marrakech in 1929, I was told that some old women would stealthily disinter corpses in the cemetery for mysterious reasons. I refused to believe it. Having come from Estonia, with a European way of thinking, I could not countenance such acts. Such tales had to be invention, a fantasy of the Arab mind — maybe widespread in oral folklore, but lacking any basis in fact.

Some years later, in 1935, I happened to glance at the local newspaper and was startled. In a matter-of-fact style, the police were reported as having caught two women in the act of busily digging up a body in a graveyard. So these macabre happenings actually went on. It said so, in black and white.

I continued to be puzzled. Why should anyone want to mess around with corpses?

In a roundabout way, I sought information from those Arab acquaintances with whom we had established a certain tie of friendship. I received no satisfactory response, but soon became convinced that the oasis city of Marrakech hardly sheltered a single person unaware of the practice. People were evasive about the reasons — they merely expressed awe at the perpetrators' stout-heartedness. Those reckless ones were not afraid of Aisha-Qandisha, the ogre who roamed the cemeteries at night. Taller than a man, she had a woman's torso, a camel's legs, and a bloody wound beneath each eye. Her eyes glowing like coals, she pursued all humans, but was particularly fond of catching men.

I began to look at cemeteries more attentively. When passing by, I would sometimes step over the crumbling wall and walk among the mounds. The Moroccan graveyards were — and still are — treeless and bushless patches of desert. Skies glassy with the glowing sun made cemeteries look like mazes of trash piles or junk heaps dug up by moles. No human hand ever cared for those haphazardly scattered mounds, and no flower ever decorated

35

them: why be concerned about earthly remains destined by Allah to decay? Only some of the most recent barrows had a tilting tile stuck into the ground at either end. Bodies were buried only a few spans deep, usually without a coffin, wrapped in cheap muslin. Nothing of value could be sought or found on them.

As I gradually became familiar with the nuances of Arabic, my ear started to catch such strange comments as:

'Mohammed is going like mad after Lila, the dancing girl. She must be feeding him kneecap.'

Another time:

'What else could Mustafa have died of but swallowing a ground tooth? And it happened right after he brought a new wife into the house, a really young one, in addition to his first wife.'

More frequently, it was said:

'These ashes are extremely potent against such and such an ailment — unfortunately they are also expensive.'

But I also overheard whispers:

'As soon as he had finished eating his dish of couscous, his guts were contorted by cramps. They probably stretched him out right next to the one whose hand had rolled the couscous granules.'

Finding a single missing letter may solve a crossword puzzle, and a single word made me grasp, one day, the meaning of all these disparate utterances. Add the word 'corpse' to the teeth, kneecaps and ashes, and you had the answer — one sought help from the dead against ailments of body and of soul.

Dead bones were to repel disease, and to help ward off witch-craft, widely practised in Morocco at that time. This practice was usually harmless, but there were many serious consequences too. Polygamy bred intrigue and quarrelling among the wives, each of whom was on the look-out for her own interests and those of her children. Small wonder, then, that the more potent cures were brought in from the graveyard, when every other means had failed to soothe despair and rage.

Due to the shallowness of the graves, it wasn't actually very difficult to pull out a few bones. One only had to be sure to pick an old grave where the sun had baked the bones through the thin covering of earth to a state of brittleness. The kneecap could easily be extracted from between the thighbone and the shinbone. It was also rather easy to crush it into powder in a mortar. The kneecap was harmless. Burned to ashes, it was suitable for controlling disease and regulating love affairs.

The tooth was more dangerous. At times, it could kill. Pound and crush it as you might, its enamel would not completely disappear. If swallowed, the slightest amount of these tiny splinters could cause lesions in the intestines, causing pain and eventually even death.

But why was the speaker's voice hushed into a whisper, at times, when mentioning couscous in my presence? Why was it called the 'couscous of the dead'? Foolishness. Couscous is the Moroccan national dish, a tasty food made of semolina and flour rolled together on a tray, using the palms of the hand and slowly adding water until larger granules form. What could this have to do with the dead?

In time this question was cleared up too. The granules of the 'couscous of the dead' were to be rolled not by living hands, but by those of a relatively fresh corpse. Deadly cadaver toxins were thus absorbed.

My newly acquired knowledge was to be supplemented almost at first-hand. While visiting the market in Guéliz, the European quarter of Marrakech, I could not help noticing an unusual couple: a uniformed French captain and his Arab common-law wife, Lalla Fatima. I knew neither of them personally, yet I had come to hear quite a lot about this lady. Fate had put me in a house next to that of Lalla Setti, who was Lalla Fatima's bosom friend. Arab blood also flowed in Lalla Setti's veins, and she too was an unwed live-in companion to a French official.

How clever she was! Lalla Setti was supremely adept at bossing her man around. With her unsophisticated natural instincts, she discovered and defused all dangers that could beset her in European surroundings. And she had provided against a rainy day by taking a lover of her own race.

My relations with Lalla Setti were those of good neighbours. We often offered each other a glass of mint tea. Lalla Fatima was

casually mentioned in many of our chats, but one day I found Lalla
Setti in a state of feverish excitement: the captain had turned Lalla
Fatima out of his house.

'But why?' I asked. 'He even has a daughter by this woman.'

The story that followed was extraordinary. Incensed by what
had happened, but also proud of her own success based on wise and
skillful handling of her mate, Lalla Setti forgot prudence. In her
confusion she trusted me with a most intimate secret about Lalla
Fatima.

It seems that the captain's relations with his mistress had got
markedly worse some time ago. All Lalla Fatima's expedients had
failed: he was turning ever more impatient and bad-tempered.
Having tried everything else, Fatima finally resorted to the ultimate remedy — to use the dead as a means of instilling submissiveness in the officer. With her mother, she stole off to the
cemetery in the dead of the night. They scraped the dirt off a
newly buried body, and then lifting it up into a sitting position,
they momentarily dressed it in the captain's uniform jacket. But
inexplicably the corpse's coolness, thus stored in the coat, was of
no use in cooling down the captain's soul. The act produced a
contrary effect: the captain went utterly wild and turned both
Lalla Fatima and her daughter out of his house.

The very next day I met the captain in the street. My feet gave a
jerk, and blood rushed into my head. He walked wearily, and the
look on his face was obtuse. Was the uniform coat he was wearing
the one that had had the macabre baptism? Like some learner-
driver irresistibly mesmerised by oncoming headlights, I could
only look at that coat. I moved towards it until, at the last
moment, disgust made me swerve to one side.

'If you only knew!' I felt like shouting at the captain. Fighting
down nausea, I rushed home with my burden of secrecy. Later I
heard that the captain had moved to France, where he was stricken
with paralysis and soon died.

About a year later I made the acquaintance of yet another nightly
visitor to graveyards, although I did not know it at first. Lalla
Hedda immediately aroused my interest. She was still quite young,

with a very fair complexion and a pleasant face, but some indefinable melancholy seemed to weigh her down. Although her smile was warm, her eyes remained sad.

I met Hedda in a friendly Moroccan home, where she used to drop in and assist the mistress of the house in working on wool. Her job was to wash the matted sheep wool of old sitting mattresses, pluck it loose, and refill the ticks with clean wool. I wondered why a Muslim woman was doing such furniture work; as a rule, it was the job of male Jews to handle those long and heavy sitting mattresses.

One day, while Lalla Hedda was working there, plucking tufts of wool apart in her usual withdrawn manner, I could not resist asking the hostess about Hedda's background.

'She's without husband or child.'

That was odd. Why would such a comely woman stay single, when ugly women, and even those with deformities, had procured a husband, making full use of the prevalent custom of not letting the groom see the bride before the wedding night?

And then the mistress of the house told me. Listening, I felt as if the words came directly from Hedda herself, at the only time when this human being had gathered enough courage to open her tormented heart to my hostess.

You know well, honourable mistress, that I am without kin. As a child, I was picked up from the street, during the Great Famine, by the widowed Lalla Tammou, so that I could run errands for her. As I grew up, I became her companion. My foster-mother evoked in me obedience and respect, which was not without fear. No one knew herbs better than she did. Making use of their beneficial or poisonous properties, she brewed remedies for various purposes. She dealt in witchcraft too, which is why I dreaded her. People came from far and near to seek her help, and the thump of the door-knocker frequently echoed in our patio.

Although two living rooms led off this patio, one of them was usually locked up. This was not done to spare the sitting mattress with its new multicoloured muslin cover; Tammou's chest of valuables was in there. It felt sinister, and I kept away from it. The

chest contained potent materials like aloe and myrrh for subduing
spirits, and coriander and leather shavings for conjuring demons.
It also contained human hair, bits of nails, and urine — and even
more efficacious ingredients out of which Tammou knew how to
brew a sensational love potion by adding the right amount of
finely-pestled Spanish flies.

At times my mistress would send me to work with Ba'aba
Bohbot, a Jew who was buying up huge amounts of herbs to sell
them overseas to the Christians. To clean and screen these herbs,
the Jew needed many hands, especially in the spring, when the
donkeys carried in entire loads of orange blossoms and rose buds,
and when the poppy flowers were heaped high in the storage shed.

At home Lalla Tammou made me pestle strange mixtures in a
mortar, and after dusk I had to pay strict attention not to step
accidentally over the mortar. Lalla Tammou gave me a stern
warning about that. You can well understand, honourable mistress, what untold misfortunes I, a parentless child, could suffer if I
strode over all that witchcraft.

Lalla Tammou was often away from home. At times she even
vanished at night, leaving me alone. I was scared and anguished
when that happened.

When I had started to grow up, a new family moved in next to
us. Their eldest son was called Larbi, and there was no handsomer
young man in the world. He had a friendly look, and when he
laughed his teeth flashed like chunks of sugar on the grocer's
counter. I observed him through a door that I held scarcely open,
as he strode to or from work, his bearing calm and self-assured.
Although his job was irrigating the fields beyond the city walls, he
wore city clothes. Once he removed his turban to rewrap it, and I
noticed that the top of his head was not shaven clean: he followed
the new fashion of letting the hair grow.

One day, coming from the public baking oven, a bread board
with the hot loaf balanced on my head, I wanted to open our house
door, but the corner of my *haik* got stuck round the knocker.
The loaf almost fell off. As I grabbed the bread board with both
hands, my *haik* unwrapped itself, uncovering my face. At that
very moment the neighbour's door flew open, and Larbi almost

bumped into me. He saw my naked countenance! Utterly ashamed, I escaped into the house. Yet from that day Larbi was different. It was odd how we now seemed to encounter each other more frequently, and I felt as if he was now keeping on the look-out. Then, as we passed in the street, he whispered:

'Oh gazelle! the light for my eyes!'

His voice, hot and sweet like mint tea, made my body glow. I began to hope that he might marry me, because his mother addressed me with increased kindliness. Pointing at me with her finger, she said meaningfully to Tammou: 'If my son wants to buy our own country's wheat, be it so! — even if it be but barley.'

Rumours flew that Larbi was saving for bride purchase money. My joy knew no bounds, and I was eagerly waiting for the matchmaker.

A haughty and corpulent lady, the oldest of the three wives of Berra'ada the merchant had become Lalla Tammou's most stead-fast client. Tammou prepared charms for her to guard against her co-wives' evil eye. I once went with my foster-mother to the cemetery around noon. With her she took the merchant's slip-pers, one filled with grain, the other with salt. After pouring the contents on a mound and placing the slippers on top of it, Tammou kept circling the grave, spinning around herself and wildly waving her arms. As we went away, we left the slippers behind. I was quivering all over, thinking about the merchant. From now on he could no longer make love with his two younger wives — the grip of the dead had drained his bodily strength.

Lately that merchant's wife had become worried again, and her visits became more frequent. Then Tammou announced that we had to go to the graveyard once more to deal with the merchant — this time for good.

The fateful day arrived. Already in the morning, my foster-mother made preparations, piling all sorts of stuff, even food, into the basket. We left in the late afternoon. To my astonishment, Tammou attached a short-handled hoe under both her caftan and mine, and, after we had gone out through the city gate, she led me to a place quite a long way from the cemetery. We sat down in the

shelter of some dense bushes and ate the bread and the dates we had
brought with us. Only when night fell did Lalla Tammou initiate
me into her plans, and I became filled with anxiety, as if someone
had squeezed my entrails. I was to help her dig up a girl who had
been buried only the day before. I was not to resist or even hesitate. Now I understood why Tammou had left home several days
in succession: she had kept watch outside the city gate for a funeral
procession to pass by.

We did not leave the bush until past midnight. There was no
sound. A new moon lay over on its back, and one could easily find
one's way about by its faint glow.

I was scared stiff, and walked close to my foster-mother. We
stepped over the low graveyard wall, and then, stumbling in the
maze of graves, we tried to make our way towards the dark mass
of some date palms. Reaching the trees, Tammou searched until
she located the mound — she had memorised where it was. Higher
and more fresh than all others, anyone could tell that it was a
recent one.

We took our hoes out from underneath our clothes, and on
harsh command from Tammou I started striking the mound along
with her to get the earth away. We soon reached the smooth
surface underneath. In spite of the darkness Tammou found the
contours of the actual pit. Its width towards each end was as usual
— one span plus four finger-widths — and around the centre it
corresponded to the width of an adult person. It did not take much
effort to shovel the gravelly dirt out of that narrow ditch, since the
grave had not yet settled. Soon my hoe banged against something
hard — one of the bricks which were laid in two rows, tilting
against each other and forming a sharp-ridged roof over the body.
We put down our hoes and, kneeling, continued tossing the dirt
out with our bare hands.

Removing the first brick was hard work, but the others came
out easily. The whitish shimmer of the shroud was now visible,
and the sight struck me with horror. Up to that point I had
worked away as if I was in a daze, but now I stiffened, and a brick
fell from between my fingers, landing on the corpse with a dark
thud.

'May Allah punish you with fever!' Lalla Tammou hissed.

The roof over the corpse's head we left intact. Tammou cautiously lowered her legs into the pit, next to the shins, and barely had room to stand on one leg. From her bosom she pulled out a candle which she lit with a match, passed it all over the length of the body, and then directed the flickering light into the niche at the head. The human shape, wrapped in muslin, was wedged into the grave, lying on its right side, so that it looked towards Mecca. I was brought to my senses by Tammou's shouting for the rope. She pulled it through underneath the corpse's shins, then she tied a knot and threw one end to me.

'We'll soon have her out!' she mumbled, climbing out of the pit on all fours. 'She found favour with Allah: look how loosely she fits into the grave. There was no need to force her in. Now we just have to keep pulling!'

Our joint efforts made the body start to move. The smoothness of the palm-leaf mat at the bottom of the grave made it slide more easily. However, the last part of the operation was complicated by the fact that the corpse had been placed on its side. Again Tammou went down into the pit, and tried to turn it over on to its back. The ditch was so narrow that she barely succeeded, and then only because the girl was so small. We battled away until the legs surfaced. Tammou jumped into the pit a third time. Gasping from the strain, she heaved the corpse while I pulled at it by the legs. At last we made it, and the shrouded corpse was spread out at the edge of the grave like a serpent in its sheath.

I was at the end of my strength. Panting and shivering all over, I closed my eyes and sat down with cold sweat on my forehead. But there was little time for resting.

'Up you get!' Tammou snapped, and I staggered to my feet again.

Tammou had cut the shroud on each side, and pulled out the girl's hands — I stared at them with an indescribable sense of ghastliness, for they were not as one would expect a corpse to be, but gruesomely yellow. A woollen thread round the wrists denoted a bride. Finally it occurred to me that the yellow was caused by saffron, a solution used by those who wash corpses to rub over the hands and faces of virgins.

'Come on!' Tammou said hoarsely. 'Help me to sit her up!'

Lifted up by the shoulders, the corpse insisted on bending forwards, and it would have dropped back into the pit if Tammou had not pushed it to lean against me.

'Hold her up!' she hissed, piercing me with her vicious glance. 'May leprosy attack your heels if you let her go!' I did not doubt the seriousness of the threat or the potency of Tammou's curse.

The torso pressed with a leaden weight against my chest. Its icy cold came through my clothes, and into the very marrow of my bones. The stench was sickening. I wanted to jump up and run away, but Tammou had already placed the sowing tray in the corpse's lap, thrown in one fistful of couscous and another of flour, and sprayed water from a bottle over the top. Seizing the arms she began to revolve these lifeless hands in circles, against the bottom of the tray. They rustled softly.

How long did the preparation of couscous granules last? I have no idea because I was on the verge of fainting when Tammou finally allowed me to set the body down. I pulled my hands away so quickly that the corpse crashed on its back, and the sweatcloth unravelled itself, revealing the face — which was a grisly saffron yellow. My knees were bending, and I felt as if my feet were growing roots to stay forever in that graveyard.

Then a diffuse distant buzz roused me from my stupor. Tammou and I listened: there was no doubt it was human voices. By now we could also hear the sound of steps — and see the silhouettes of three men moving straight toward us. Were they some irrigators of the fields returning home from the night shift and emboldened by 'safety in numbers' to take a short cut through the cemetery?

They stopped. Had they been disturbed by something? Had the faint glow of the candle deep down in the pit given us away? After hesitating a moment, they came on towards us. We panicked.

'Push!' said Tammou, 'push that offspring of dogs into the pit!'

We shoved with all our might, and down it went, head first

and half-bent. Tammou pushed two candles into my hand: 'Light them!' She grabbed a hoe, covered it with her white *haik*, and lifted it high above her head. With the other hand she held the two candles in front of the *haik*. I got it: this object was to represent the fiery-eyed demon head turning Tammou into the high-necked Aisha-Qandisha.

In this guise, she reeled towards the intruders, and two of them immediately turned on their heels and ran. The third, more courageous, stood his ground. I heard him pronounce the formula to repel demons: *'Besmellah rahman rahim!'*

I knew this voice! Where had I heard it before? Allah, Allah, it could not be. . . . Yes, it was Larbi.

Once more, Larbi implored God for help. Fear overcame him. The bogey woman was all set to drag him away, and satisfy her lust right there among the mounds. Never again would he see his home and his mother. The bogey would bury him alive in this graveyard.

'A tool made of steel!' The thought flashed simultaneously through my mind and Larbi's. Cutting steel — the only way to defeat Aisha-Qandisha!

It all happened fast as lightning. In a few bounds Larbi rushed up, something whistled through the air, and Tammou's fearful scream resounded through the cemetery. Struck down, she howled like a dog caught under a cartwheel. Her voice too must have sounded somewhat familiar, because Larbi stepped closer.

'You' he cried, appalled. 'Lalla Tammou!' The two neighbours stared at each other.

'So it's you, you damned bastard!' Tammou bawled. 'Curses to you! May a bullet strike you! May your guts be torn to pieces! You interrupted my work, and you cut my hand off with your spade!'

'And what are you doing here?'

'May hell's fires parch you!' Tammou writhed in pain. 'What was I doing? I was turning a child round in the right position. It had been buried carelessly, face down and so its mother could not bear other children. Out of the goodness of my heart I came to readjust that child — and now you have killed me. Curse you!'

But Larbi went to the pit. His glance took in the adult body, and the couscous tray — it was all as clear as daylight. At one swoop he tore off my *haik*. His face was hard and grim. Kicking the couscous aside, he jumped into the pit, and set the corpse on its side.

'Pull the legs straight!' he told me, and his words were like whiplashes.

And then the most horrible event of all. . . . In my haste to obey Larbi's command, and confused as I was, I stepped over the grave. At once the consciousness of my terrible position pierced me like a red-hot skewer. Astride above an open grave, worthy mistress! Happiness was now to be excluded for ever from my life. There was no more point in pouring my heart out to Larbi — explanations and reconciliations were of no use when I could not any longer make a fitting wife for him, or for any other man. Striding over the grave had turned me barren. No child could ever be conceived in my womb. Never.

Larbi quickly filled in the pit and left. We hobbled home, I burdened by the basket full of tools and by my tormented soul, and Tammou moaning and nursing her hand.

The very next night I fled and sought shelter with Ba'aba Bohbot's wife to serve her in exchange for a crumb of bread. Living among the Jews — that's where I learned the wool trade. Lalla Tammou's hand shrivelled away. Now she begs on street corners.

And how could I, a minor slave, avoid the fate that Allah had assigned to me? Faced with the inevitable, I can only say: humans cannot escape the alternation of day and night, nor can they escape death. Let us be submissive to Him.

I should supplement the notes I made at that time by mentioning two much later events. Despite the fact that the graveyard walls had been raised higher and guards had been hired, a newspaper in Marrakech reported in 1959 that a corpse had been dug out. The same year in March a human skeleton used for anatomy lessons at the French high school in Casablanca vanished from a classroom without a trace.

Are we entitled to react with contempt to such happenings? For we follow in the footsteps of those who use corpses for magic by exchanging our dimmed corneas for those of the dead, and by acquiring their hearts and other organs.

THE BATHS
(1935)

The invitation to the baths came when we had finished rubbing Lalla Hnia's congested chest with the pharmacist's ointment. The job had kept us all busy, starting with the *tbib* and ending with half-a-dozen female helpers. The *cadi*'s dominant wife had a cold.

'It smells good,' noted Lalla Hadoum, the *cadi*'s second wife, who knelt in front of the patient. She pulled Lalla Hnia's rolled-up caftans still higher over her face and inhaled deeply from the spicy unguent.

The co-wife's pretty sixteen-year-old daughter Lalla Nafissa squatted on the rug, helping to support the patient. She turned to her mother, revealing all her bright teeth in a smile:

'It smells wonderful now, but what if later it starts to smart and smoulder like fire?'

Becoming serious again, she tenderly kissed the mistress's hand:

'Allah be merciful to you, Lalla Hnia!'

But there was no time for conversation. It was November; the spacious and lofty women's chamber was chilly, and the doctor urged us to hurry. Nafissa's younger sister dashed out with a black servant girl, and at once they returned, one with an earthen chafing dish and the other with a rough bath towel. Two black and two white hands, covered with rings, held the towel briefly over the glowing charcoal to warm. Then the helpers quickly wrapped it around Lalla Hnia's barrel-like torso.

The cure soon brought results. The wheezing and gasping Lalla Hnia hardly had time to free her head caught in the skirt flaps, lift herself up in to a sitting position, and put on her gold-embroidered belt when the smouldering skin made her shoulders twitch. Her face puckered, she rose and waddled out of the room in all her impressive width without word.

The *cadi* had of course monitored the whole process of the cure, smugly crouching on a sitting mattress near the door. Now he smiled as if freed from anguish, struck his grey beard in a characteristic genial move of his white hand, rolled his ponderous body to one side so that he could lever himself up with his elbows, and said:

'Allah be praised. Let's go and have tea.'

He beckoned us to follow him to the men's chamber on the opposite side of the patio, where three men, with the hoods of their loose white robes pulled over their turbans, were waiting: the *cadi*'s grown-up son, his brother — a gaunt, mild-mannered merchant — and his swarthy, youngish secretary Sidna Shih. They sat cross-legged, except for the *cadi* whose corpulence forced him to leave his legs stretched out straight. This pleasant and venerable grey-bearded man with his pinkish face and his thick embroidered socks had something about him of a Santa Claus.

When we had finished sipping two of the traditional three glasses of tea, the *cadi* put his empty glass on the rug at his feet, tightened the chaplet with wooden beads around his wrist, and waddled ponderously to us, settling himself like a sack next to me. His talk was brief:

'Monday evening you will come to the baths with us. Take your servant with you.'

We were speechless with surprise — that we, Christians, were being invited to go to the baths with Muslims! Didn't every tourist handbook spell it out: 'Non-Muslims are warned not to cross the threshhold of baths and mosques.' Humbly heeding this advice, I had always skirted the open portals of the city's holy places and baths (which were also under the jurisdiction of the mosques' administration), squinting at them only out of the corner of my eye so as not to desecrate them with my direct glance. And now this proposal!

We accepted with thanks. Only gradually did our thoughts crystallise into concern: how would it turn out? Might the other patrons of the baths not chase us out with boiling water, as had recently happened to a Jewess who had furtively tried to share the Arab warmth? And how hygienic was it, given that the washing was said to take place in floor-level togetherness? As if sensing our concern, the *cadi* reassured us:

'There will be no one apart from my household. I have reserved the baths for the whole night. They will bring me the key towards the evening.'

Discussing the situation later at home, my husband and I agreed that our friend the judge had not acted with rashness but rather had wisely taken everything into account. Although he was prepared to demonstrate his friendship toward us, he was not oblivious of his salvation either. Ramadan, the great Muslim fasting period, would begin on Tuesday, the very next day after the invitation date. Thus the issue of whether it was sinful to bring Christians to the baths melted away: the fast would cancel out all of the *cadi*'s errors and sins, and one more or less on our account would not matter.

Our servant Lalla Fatna was overcome with joy and pride, and with worry over preparations:

'Allah help us,' she moaned. 'How can you go to the baths when you are stark naked? There is not a single *fota* in the house. What will you put around you?' And the enterprising Lalla Fatna stuck her feet in her slippers, rushing off to buy *fotas*, those large rough towels which are wrapped around the loins in the baths.

On Monday evening a whole pile of accessories was heaped in front of us: *fotas* to cover our nakedness, basins for water, kerchiefs to cover the head, sheets for stretching out on the floor and other sheets for drying ourselves, two footstools for sitting, and of course the indispensable perfume bottle and pestled cloves to scent our hair. I myself contributed a nice pink soap and an Estonian bathing sponge I had kept as a souvenir from my own homeland in the north. We set out for the *cadi*'s house fully kitted out.

His patio was already in darkness. I joined the women in their chamber lit with a chandelier. At the opposite end of the elongated patio the men's chamber was also lit. The side chambers were dark: why waste electricity on a bath day?

The men immediately set out for the baths, wandering from the host's chamber into the patio and vanishing into the hallway. They were headed by Ali, a square-shouldered black carrying a mountain of mattresses and rugs on his head. Bought as a slave in times past, he now had a respected position as doorguard and the buyer of food for the household. Men had priority for baths as for everything else. We women had to wait for our turn.

The baths were not far away and seemed to be large, given the extent of the outer wall. This wall actually started at the judge's door, descending around the corner to a vaulted passage and ending on a small but noisy plaza. The baths had two doors: one for men, one for women. Men entered from the plaza through the public lavatories, which in fact constituted the vestibule of the baths. Unashamedly, I once cast an eye in there: a spacious cemented courtyard with an elongated pool in the centre and open compartments all around. The plaza itself was lined with barber's shops which had nets in place of doors. When leaving the baths, men could have their heads shaved clean with a knife, and the barber could also rewrap collapsed turbans. The women's entrance was a narrow and half-hidden door in the archway, but it was still out of our reach. We had to wait.

I inspected the women in the room. About ten of them were sitting or stretched out along the wall: some live-in relatives, servants with concubine status, the widows of the *cadi*'s two brothers, and the doorguard's wife. There was also the nurse, an old black woman with a cheerful wrinkled face, who at different times had lulled all the *cadi*'s children to sleep. Which of those women were coming to the baths, and which preferred staying at home?

Mine was the place of honour between the two wives, facing the door which stood wide open. On my left Lalla Hnia looked as if she were sitting on a throne; she was the real ruler of the house, firmly in charge of all the twenty-five members of the household, including in some ways even the *cadi* himself. The middle-aged Lalla Hadoum on my right had a fair measure of black blood, and in contrast to Lalla Hnia this second wife was light of foot and reacted quickly in conversation. She had a lively mind — and a Singer sewing machine. The younger women crowded in one end of the room, heads together: Lalla Hnia's only daughter and Lalla Hadoum's two. Their hair was unbraided — clearly in preparation for the baths. Tiny Miriam, the *cadi*'s niece, was skipping around the room in a satin gown which reached to the floor. She was also bound for the baths, since the hundreds of tiny braids that usually formed a pattern on her head had been unravelled.

The roomful of women waited in silence. A quarter of an hour, half an hour and longer passed, and yet no one felt the urge to talk. What was the point of pulling thoughts out of one's brain when one was busy waiting? Since childhood they had been trained to wait; this was a habitual way of passing the time. Yes, waiting was something the people in this country knew how to do in an exemplary way, with full self-control. And when they felt like it, they could fall asleep at a moment's notice. I recalled being told of prisoners who could shorten their dull existence by sleeping away half the day in unperturbed peace of mind.

Lalla Hnia still had her cold. She coughed incessantly beside me and wiped her dripping nose. A pink blanket covering her log-like legs kept slipping off and she had to pull it up again — but this was not easy, given her size. Her fingers could barely reach to grasp the hem of the blanket, and the effort made her mouth sink into her pasty double chin.

But wasn't this the pretty Lalla Douzha, the newly-wed spouse of the first wife's son, entering from the patio? She bowed down to her mother-in-law, kissed her, greeted me, and sat very quietly near the door. Lalla Douzha was not coming to the baths; she was covered with gold, a row of bracelets adorning her plump white arms, and with a pair of golden earrings. Her velvet-flowered blue *dfina* dropped lightly to the ground, covering her rose-coloured broadcloth caftan. But why had the mischievously gay Lalla Douzha been behaving lately as if her mother-in-law's presence petrified her? I could guess the reason: she had now been married for several months, yet there was no child on the way. Her mother-in-law's reproaches must rankle with her.

Incredibly, it was Lalla Hadoum and my servant Lalla Fatna who broke the silence. Their talk was about the quantity of cloth needed for caftans. Lalla Fatna felt ignorant in this area and profited from the opportunity to garner some useful tips. Measuring caftan tails with their arms, they discussed and calculated, the onlookers following their conversation lazily through half-closed eyelids.

It was a chilly November evening and I had followed the example of the others and pulled my legs up under me. Yet, stubbornly, both sides of the lofty door were kept open. To pass the time, I looked around the patio. The arched doorway leading into the men's chamber carved a bright picture out of the surrounding darkness: a plastered wall high above, the red rug below, and the multi-coloured band of the wall panel and the sitting mattresses in the middle. The marble of the patio shone dimly, and banana leaves cast flickering shadows on the wall. The fountain in the centre faded altogether into the darkness, its existence suggested only by the luminous edge of the basin. A cat skulked along the path, and with one bound, it dissolved into the dark bushes. For how much longer would I have to go on counting the black and white tiles in the patio? Like the others, I shrank down and leaned my head against the wall.

The patio was suddenly pervaded by the chatter of voices: the men were back. Wrapped in burnouses, they returned to the opposite room. Only the *cadi*'s son, perspiring and red in the face, rushed past us to give orders to the kitchen. Woman servants immediately hurried to the men's chamber with tea kettles and platters. It was our turn to go to the baths. To my surprise, Lalla Hnia stood up first.

'*Besmellah!* In the name of God,' she intoned and seemed to give the departure signal by pulling the rug which had covered her legs up over her head. A large collection of *haiks* surrounded me in the patio; some had come from our room, others from the kitchen, others from heaven knows where. Lalla Douzha stayed behind, leaning against the door frame. Like a religious procession we walked slowly to the street. In the archway a glow of fire reached us from a low door, and I looked in. Far down at the bottom of a cavernous cellar human forms moved like dark shadows in front of the opening of a blazing furnace — piles of palm leaves were used as firewood.

'This is the furnace room of the baths,' Lalla Nafissa shouted. We reached the women's door. Ali had escorted us, carrying a huge key; he turned it in the keyhole, and the wooden-hinged door creaked open.

I stood before a long dim passage. Falling on to the whitewashed wall, high up on my left, small rectangles of light seemed like giant-sized data tables filled with a shadowy script. These were projected by small oil lamps burning behind spiral-patterned grids in niches built into the wall. Further along, the passage faded away into the dark. Its sloping floor had steps at intervals so that I could only go forward one step at a time. Suddenly we came to the end of the right-hand wall: we were in an astonishingly spacious church-like hall — was this no more than the centre of baths? A decorous fountain was surrounded by towering columns shielding rush mats which glimmered on the floor along the walls.

The servants were already heading for the mats. This must be the dressing room, since *haiks* were dropped and nimble fingers started removing the remaining clothes. Brown shadows soon slipped past me, vanishing behind a side door; it must lead to the washing area.

Brrr . . . it was too cold here for undressing. I tried to make out whether this place was an open patio such as the one found at the centre of all Moorish homes. Casting a probing eye upwards, I found it was covered. Phantasmal contours high above showed curves and jags: the central part, supported on columns, was crowned with a splendid dome of carved wood. These baths, I found, were ancient — they had been in service for 645 years.

The *cadi*'s wives and daughters had settled in a compartment set aside by a partition and lighted with a brighter lamp. Mattresses and cushions brought along from home made it seem tiny. It was here we were to get undressed. The thin *dfina* was pulled over the head, followed by the broadcloth caftans. In cold weather two of these were worn one on top of the other. The high-collared white cotton petticoat or overall came off next, leaving only long-sleeved singlets and dark thick baggy trousers with embroidered lace; these were tight below the knees and formed hundreds of folds at the seat. At this stage of *déshabillé* the Lallas looked very much like their men. The trousers were next to go; you then wrapped a *fota* around your loins.

The marble floor felt as cold as a skating rink. I tiptoed to the threshold of the washing room, my shoulders and even my nose covered with the *fota*. The heavy door thumped behind me. I expected steam; was it so thick that nothing else was visible? But there was no steam at all. High up in the wall niche, the anaemic rays of a minute oil lamp could not disperse the shadows of the long narrow vault which I had to cross sideways. Its left end looked like the entrance to a dark tunnel, and the room was bare, except for an open basin like a trough adjoining the lamplit wall. The surface of the flowing cold water had a leaden gleam that made us shiver.

'Come, move on!' Lalla Nafissa was escorting me. 'This room is used for washing only during the summer heat.'

We entered another vault, as long as the previous one but much wider. The high arched ceiling was supported by a row of three columns. Here, too, a tiny light quivered high up in a hole in the right wall. I began to grasp the basic floor plan: the larger dimension of the washing rooms corresponded to the side of the adjoining covered patio where we undressed, and the flickering lamps were the same ones I had observed earlier from the hallway.

The second washing room was also bare and empty, but there one could already detect the stuffy scent of the baths: a mix of tepid warmth, the scent of oil, and a hint of perspiration from previous customers.

On we went through the next door. Another vault, narrow like a tongue, but at last — thank God! — warm and cosy. I must be catching up with my hosts, judging from the rattle of pails and the muted buzz of conversation. Nafissa pulled open the fourth door.

'*Yu-yu-yu!*' The greeting whoop of the doorguard's wife resounded throughout the vault. I was received with laughter and shouting as I slowly made my way among bodies stretched out on the dimly-lit floor. Hands took hold of my *fota*.

'Go, sit down there!' — 'No, come and stretch down right here!'

The washing room looked like a dark water-colour painting after someone had gone over it with a wet sponge: the contours were diffuse and the colours smudged. Vague human forms walked, sat or reclined. The floor was full of voluminous wooden buckets with rope handles, not quite of the kind used in Estonia and Finland for saunas. My servant Lalla Fatna touched my shoulder and pointed to the footstool she had brought along: 'You can sit on that.'

'No!' This was Lalla Hadoum herself. 'Not on the stool but on the ground. The floor is warm.' She was not used to being contradicted and pulled me beside her on the sheet. Lalla Hadoum was right: the floor was wonderfully warm. Further away the servants milled around, returning buckets full of water. That wall must have had warm and cold water outlets, maybe even taps fixed to the end of pipes.

Used to the Estonian sauna, I looked in vain for the furnace. The air was dry. Of course, this was a Turkish bath where heating comes up through the floor. We were sitting right above the same furnace I had seen earlier from the street. It was like sitting on top of a volcano, hoping there would be no eruption, but having seen how baths were built, I did not need to worry. The rugged brick vaulting above the fire was topped by a ten-inch layer of salt, over which lay a layer of lime – the floor – which had been pounded to a mirrorlike smoothness. Insulated from the fire by three protective layers, I was not so much being cooked as wallowing in blissful comfort.

Such idling is an agreeable occupation, but it was time for washing. I produced my aromatic pink soap and politely offered it to Lalla Hadoum. Hesitantly, she accepted it, sniffed at it once, and put it on the floor far away from her. I offered the scorned object to other people, but surprisingly no one would take it — I only got apprehensive glances. No problem. If they do not like it, I do! So I dipped the soap in water, built up foam in my sponge, and got set for rubbing myself, when Lalla Hadoum clutched her fingers around my wrist. Her alarmed eyes close to my face, she exclaimed:

'Drop it! I tell you: put it away right now!'

What was troubling her? Were baths not meant for washing? Without further ado Lalla Hadoum snatched the soap from my hand and threw it into the furthest and darkest corner. She then seized my sponge and it followed the same trajectory. Then, after rinsing her hands, she snapped at me, partly scolding, partly admonishing:

'You may die if you rub your body with that stuff. Don't you know that such soap is poisonous?'

For a while I was dumbfounded. Then I felt angry: damn it, my sponge from Estonia! I certainly would not give up such a precious memento, but would get it back, using a tiger's boldness and a serpent's guile — not now, but later.

'Use that!' Lalla Hadoum threw something which fell rattling at my feet. I lifted up a stone, rather a flat piece of brick. Was I supposed to scrub myself with this? Lalla Hadoum shook her head as though she were dealing with an imbecile. She called a servant girl, who came and crouched in front of me. She placed my leg in her lap, immobilising it with her iron grip. Then she started to work on my soles with the brick, as if it were a grater. So this was the purpose of the brick! I pulled my leg away: 'Just a moment! I'd rather do it myself.'

And so we kept scraping soles, be they our own or someone else's. This is an essential task for those whose heels have become hard as horn from wearing heelless slippers. Nafissas's sister seemed to be the laziest among us; she lay on her stomach, enjoying the moment to the full with one servant working away at each of her feet. Suddenly I became conscious of the heat: the temperature in a Moorish bath is oddly deceptive, heating you up imperceptibly as if by stealth. My body was wet all over, with the perspiration trickling down my shins. Now I understood why they started with the sole-scraping: this is a lengthy task, and meanwhile the skin can steam.

What had been the effect of the heat on the first wife's cold? Lalla Hnia and her daughter were hidden in the darkness, with servants thronging around them. Nafissa explained that the female bath attendant had now finished massaging Lalla Hnia's aching muscles. She would usually do the same to all the women in the party, but today there was no time. I vaguely sensed rather than actually saw the first wife's whitish contours; the tiny lamp, its light like the eye of a mouse, was faithful to its task, casting such a miserly light that one's nakedness was concealed. Looking at another's naked body is sinful and has been so since the creation of the world. Noah's two sons in the Old Testament knew it already; when they saw their drunken father snoozing half-naked, they approached him backwards to cover him up with a cloak. That command of Allah was still obeyed in those baths.

However, the incitement of the Evil One made me keep my eyes wider open than usual, and I could not help but notice some mysterious activity in progress. Stealthily, as if ashamed, the women were passing round a small bowl, and applying its mushy contents to the hair in the armpits and elsewhere with a wooden spatula.

'That horrible *zerneeh*,' Nafissa's sister cursed and whined. 'It starts smarting right away. It brings my skin out in blisters, without fail.'

'But using a knife is no better, with all the stubble it leaves,' her mother quieted her. 'Just try rinsing it off quicker.' They did not offer me the bowl. The Christian had no business with the customs and requirements of Islam: people must not have any hair anywhere except, for a woman, on her head for beauty and, for a man, on his chin for dignity.

Only now did the actual washing begin. All the matrons and young ladies were stretched out on the floor, each attended by a servant. So this was why so many servants were brought along. There was one for me too.

I cast glances towards my soap and sponge — where were these friends of mine? The servant who washed me did not need them; she did the job with a light round piece of palmwood covered with a net. She started scrubbing me competently and forcefully, from the neck down to the feet, skimming off the epidermis which had become easy to remove after soaking in sweat. The task was completed rapidly and without leaving a single scratch, because the piece of wood and its cover had been previously softened up in water. After being rinsed with a bucketful of water, I was left sparklingly clean.

The heat was getting to be too much. Lalla Hnia and some others retreated to the cooler antechamber, and the rest gradually followed. The nurse waddled past me, holding the happily squeaking Miriam by the hand. She was broad in the beam — the *fota* had slipped off and trailed behind her. Heedless of God's command I looked straight at her: she must have been like her parents, black slaves imported from the Sudan. Her stout body was oddly thin at the waist; her long drooping breasts reached her stomach. The massive buttocks had a peculiar shape — high and flat-topped; they combined with her back to form something like a chair. Had not all the babies in the *cadi*'s family fallen asleep astride this back, tied around her body with their noses pressed against her protective back?

I waited impatiently for the room to empty so that I could execute my secret plan of retrieving the sponge. I pretended to be the last out, then at the door quietly turned back. Like a thief I slipped into the darkness of the vault where the sponge must have landed. I had to be quick before anyone could spot me. Moving around on my hands and knees I raked the floor with my fingers: it had to be somewhere. At last — luck was with me — I felt the sponge, slipped it into my *fota*, and hurried back to the other room where my companions were busy washing their hair.

'You really don't want to leave the heat.' Lalla Nafissa laughed at me, and her teeth of milky whiteness shone in the semi-darkness. 'Come, sit down in front of me and give me your head.' She personally applied a natural shampoo, a clay called *rassoul*, to my hair, using a brass container full of the substance. At home that morning the crumbling clods of *rassoul* had been tied up in a rag and left soaking in water until they disintegrated into a sludge. This was poured into a flat dish, and human palms had rubbed out all sand grains and stone splinters. Now Lalla Nafissa smeared my hair with this sticky brown mush. Then she added water and scrubbed it thoroughly. Finally she started the rinsing, tossing one bucketful of water after another at my head so that I could scarcely breathe. But the girl knew her job: my hair would not become soft like silk unless the last traces of *rassoul* were removed.

As water carrier we had a tiny black girl of about six, lean but muscular. Her matted stack of hair was still dry. Everyone else was finishing up, but she had not even had time to wet herself, being at everybody else's beck and call. As she brought us water, she stared at me with wide-open eyes as if I were a boa constrictor. Like others, she had heard stories that the bodies of Christians were made differently from those of Muslims, and she was now looking for evidence.

Suddenly, a thunderous noise reverberated from the vaults — someone was pounding on the door with fists. It seemed that the *cadi* had sent Ali to tell us to hurry: the men wanted to start eating. Everyone was now in a flurry — the master's orders had to be obeyed without delay. After the last hasty rinsing, we donned our *fotas* and rushed back to the chilly central patio to dress. The younger ones still found time to gather around me, and I gave a rapid explanation of every piece of clothing I put on. Astonishment was written in their faces: why didn't my shirt have sleeves? Panties produced loud chuckles: did these qualify as pants? Allah! Lalla Hadoum should sew you a decent pair, using three metres of cloth! The bra passed from hand to hand and seemed to meet with some approval. Still the doorguard's wife asked me why I had bought the bra merely as an empty shell, without those pink breasts she had seen it draped over in the shop window of a Christian. As she spoke, she was dousing her head copiously with rose water from a bottle. But the real gust of laughter came at the sight of my stockings: who could have believed that those flimsy things could be of such grotesque length! The general conclusion was that my clothing was scanty and deficient.

'You poor thing! Let's at least make sure your head is kept warm.' Lalla Hadoum felt sorry for me and combined two kerchiefs into a turban, so tightly bound that I could hardly move my head. Lalla Hnia was already up. 'Let's go!' she ordered curtly. The others fell clumsily in line, and it was back to the corridor and then into the street.

The men had been slumbering half-sitting and half-lying. But sleepiness had changed into impatience. I was asked to join them and received the indispensable refreshments of someone freshly returned from baths: a glass of chocolate milk and a peeled egg richly covered with pestled cumin. As a non-Muslim guest I then joined the men for the dinner eaten from a common dish.

After dinner, as his secretary was plugging fresh mint leaves into the teapot, the *cadi* yawned and announced:

'The baths were pleasant, Allah be praised. Now Those Others can have the bath chambers for the rest of the night.' 'Those

Others'! This was the indirect designation for ghosts. Did the judge really still believe in them? I hazarded a question:

'Do they still exist nowadays?'

'Can there be any doubt?' The secretary taxed me, looking somewhat annoyed: 'The Koran does not lie. Besides, I have seen them myself.'

'Please tell me,' I insisted.

'It is well known that they are especially fond of baths. Once I went there late in the evening when the daytime customers had left. I locked the outer door and began to wash myself. Suddenly I saw a man rushing past me into the furthest chamber. I did not pay attention to him until it occurred to me that I had locked the door. At the same moment the man returned, crossed the floor again without saying a word, and vanished the way he had come. What else could it have been but a spirit? I felt as if hot tar had been poured over me. I left the baths as quickly as I could.'

'Yes, there are more bad ones than good ones among them,' the *cadi* mumbled wrinkling his eyebrows, and his fingers began dashing over the beads of his rosary.

As we left, we shook the *cadi*'s hand with sincere thanks. An Estonian and a Moroccan had washed together in the baths. It was like American Indians smoking the pipe of peace.

Dropping in to the women's chamber to say good-bye, I found that the mattresses had been laid out to form a single large circular bed. They lay along the walls like mummies, the feet of one up against the head of another, each with her *haik* pulled snugly over the head and covering the whole body. I retreated and slipped out through the piece of cloth hung over the door.

WOMAN'S CUNNING
Two tales told by Sidna Shih and the Cadi
(1935)

Sidna Shih, the *cadi*'s secretary, assumed a meditative pose, cross-legged and with his head slightly lowered. He closed his eyes for a moment and then started in a soft voice:

Allah akbar! God is great. Once a Moroccan scholar decided to make a study of woman's cunning. The task was complex, but he expected to succeed. He intended to write up his results as a book which would be welcome and needed by all Moroccan men (here Sidna Shih hesitated, glanced slyly at the *tbib*, and smirked), and probably by the European men as well.

The scholar intended to lay bare the soul of a woman and penetrate its most secret recesses. He intended to attack with special tenacity her intrigues, which were like a tangled ball of yarn, with no perceivable beginning or end. Woman's cunning schemes all too often deprived men of their peace of mind. Yet women always managed to avoid the blame and look as if they were in the right. Despite their power and wisdom, men became entangled in the invisible net knotted by their spouses and could find no reason to chastise them.

The results were to profit the scholar himself first of all. Up till then he had avoided the chains of marriage, but with his study completed he could admit one or even several wives to his household without any worry, along with their servants. He would be safe: they would not be able to undermine the foundations of his domestic tranquility, and they could not darken the philosopher's existential firmament with their cunning.

So far so good. (Sidna Shih gave a cough and pushed his turban further back from his brow.) The scholar locked himself into his house and set to work. Soon the whole city knew about his project, and every male heart was filled with hope. Passers-by would automatically walk more softly as they reached the sage's door, and drivers of donkeys would desist from their coarse shouts so that no unnecessary noise would penetrate over the wall into his patio and disturb him in his work.

The scholar spent long hours on the pillows, pondering the soul of woman. He would walk in the patio without noticing the fresh blooms of the mimosa. The crisp evening air smoothed his forehead, and the stars above him stimulated his flights of thought.

One day, as he was taking his customary walk in the shadow of the patio walls and his glance was raised to the evening sky, something startled him. The figure of a woman wrapped in a *haik* was leaning over the edge of the flat roof above his head. Before the scholar had time to regain his composure a sweet voice reached his ears:

'Peace be with you, O scholar! May Allah pour some of His wisdom into you at this evening hour.' Then she pulled herself sharply back from the edge and was gone. The scholar shook his head with dismay. What behaviour! What moral degeneration! Of course, after dusk the city's flat roofs belong to the women, but how impudent it was to look into another household's courtyard and furthermore to address a male stranger!

Yet it happened a second time the very next evening. Again the woman made her melodious greeting, and as she rearranged her *haik*, her henna-decorated hand and snow-white arm emerged from the folds of white cloth.

On the third evening the scholar was surprised to discover that he was actually waiting for her. He even smiled back at the woman's greeting and no longer condemned her. The woman said:

'Please forgive a feeble woman who, driven by admiration, dares to strike with her humble glance your brow shining with glory. Oh, do tell your slave what is stirring in your noble head and what thoughts are visiting your high-minded brain?'

'I am studying the reasons behind woman's cunning and intrigues.'

'Allah is great and mighty! O scholar, has your arduous and venerable inquiry already brought results?'

'With Allah's help I have made good progress and soon hope to conclude my study, O daughter of the faithful!'

'May Allah compensate you for your pains sevenfold!' the stranger exclaimed enthusiastically, and vanished.

She came again and again, and from one evening to the next the scholar's response became warmer. Then the day arrived when he proudly announced to her:

'I have completed my study. Every single aspect is clear to me.'

'Allah be praised!' the woman cried, and she . . . (Sidna Shih's easy-flowing account suddenly came to a halt. His expression became oddly helpless. Casting a covert glance toward the *cadi*, he swallowed and, gathering his courage, quickly blurted out the rest.)

Yes, the woman . . . The woman pulled the veil off her face. (Having got over this awkward sentence, Sidna Shih's swarthy face became enlivened, and the corners of his mouth turned upwards in a chuckle. He made a sound like a hiccup.) The woman was . . . so fair . . . so beautiful . . . . (He started to search for adequate terms.)

Her countenance was white like milk, her eyes were shining stars, her mouth like a field poppy. Her smile, so full of modesty, was sweet like the scent of orange tree blossoms. Never before had the scholar seen such beauty and charm.

'Who are you?' he asked. 'I want to marry you. Tell me who is your father, and I'll immediately dispatch the matchmakers.'

'O scholar, have I really found grace in your eyes? I would be thankful merely for being allowed to serve you as a slave. My father is a well-known tea and sugar merchant, and he lives only a few houses away. But be forewarned, O scholar, that taking me in marriage will not be a simple task. My father is proud of my beauty and will not easily accept just any suitor. When he hears that you are a scholar rather than an immensely rich merchant he will cunningly try to convince you that I am the ugliest girl under the sun. But don't be deterred and don't tire before you have his consent and you have both signed the marriage contract in the *cadi*'s presence.'

The very next day the scholar sent the matchmaker woman to the tea merchant, and the father's reaction was as predicted. He declared his daughter the ugliest being under the sun, and only after the greatest perseverance by the matchmaker did he finally consent to give her in marriage to the scholar.

The wedding day soon came. At nightfall the scholar entered his betrothed's chamber. There she was sitting under a thick veil, that gazelle to put all other gazelles to shame. With a single pull the bridegroom removed the veil — and froze, staring at the maiden as if someone had hit him over the head. Facing him was the ugliest woman the earth has ever supported. (Sidna Shih covered his face with his hands as if he himself had received the blow. Then he continued in an incensed tone.)

Yes, that was awful. Gloomily the scholar waited for the seven-day wedding to come to an end. He was racking his brains as to how he could get rid of this repulsively ugly wife. But had not the bride's father given him plenty of warning? Under what pretext could he now ask for a divorce? As he was thus sitting and worrying in his patio at dusk, he suddenly heard again the familiar greeting from the roof. The scholar jumped on his feet in rage, all set to launch the most vicious epithets to the face of that false woman, but the maiden beat him to the word:

'I realise you are angry with me and think I am depraved. Yet it's all your own fault. How could I suppose that you would still take my words at face value after you had completed your investigation, and everything about woman's cunning was crystal-clear to you? But now, honoured scholar, you must get rid of that ugly wife pretty quick. You don't see any way out? But it's all very simple. Tomorrow morning you both don beggar's clothes and start begging for alms in the souks. When people wonder why a renowned scholar and the daughter of a wealthy merchant should go and beg, you simply answer: "I married a girl much too ugly, and now I have lost all pleasure and happiness. Begging will help to dull my pain." You will see how quickly you get rid of your wife.'

Put to shame but glad to find some way out, the scholar did not wait a single day before going out to beg with his wife. The wife's wealthy father heard about his daughter's humiliation and sent her word to return to his home.

After that, the scholar married the most beautiful and most

cunning of them all. He burned his manuscript and announced publicly that no man alive is sufficiently wise to cope with the secret schemes of women. Great is Allah's power!

Now the *cadi* spoke:

In the name of Allah the mighty and merciful! Allah's blessing be with all the listeners and story-tellers!

Once there lived a judge who always decided in favour of women. Regardless of whether the man or the woman was the guilty party, the woman always triumphed at the end. Women would beg at the court and weep imploringly, while men would demand their rights heatedly and sometimes even overbearingly. Finally, the *cadi*'s own wife decided to educate her spouse regarding woman's cunning skills of make-believe.

It was the *cadi*'s custom to invite his friends over for dinner every week on the holy day of Friday. One Friday afternoon, as he returned home from prayer at the mosque, a disagreeable surprise made him stop and frown: no preparations whatever had been made to receive the guests! The patio was unswept and rubbish was lying about. The main room had no rugs, and the cushions on the sitting mattresses were in disarray. The *cadi* dashed to the women's section of the house and found his wife sitting by the patio wall and breast-feeding her son. No servant was to be seen, and when the *cadi* looked into the kitchen he saw to his dismay that the coals were cold. The ashes in the hearth were grey, not red. The *cadi* angrily raised his voice. Why are his orders suddenly being disregarded? Has the *shitan*, Satan, struck the lady of the house with blindness? What excuses can he now make to his friends? How can he cleanse his person and his house of this unheard-of shame?

As if fed up with the master's reproaches, the *cadi*'s wife suddenly got up, hurried to the well, lifted up the child in her hands, and hurled him down the well. She turned and shouted at him: 'Do you think I was sitting idle? You could see for yourself that I was breast-feeding. But since you did not like it, I threw your son down the well.'

With a cry of despair, the *cadi* ran to the well, but it was deep and narrow like a pipe. He could only see the black glitter of water far below, and no trace of the child. Imploring Allah's assistance he rushed out and went to the house of his wife's parents to tell them that their daughter had gone mad.

When the *cadi* returned in the company of his father-in-law and some male relatives, he thought he must be dreaming. The patio was sparkling clean, and the main room floor was covered with multi-coloured rugs. Going to the women's quarters in astonishment, he found the women's patio and the kitchen full of bustling servants. Dishes in clay containers were lined up in ranks next to the well, waiting to be served, and on the tray the teapot covered with a veil gave off an aroma of mint. The *cadi*'s wife came smilingly to meet him, their little son in her arms.

'You have gone mad yourself,' the father-in-law said, and one could see from their eyes that his retinue shared his opinion. The *shitan*'s servants had succeeded in blurring the *cadi*'s mind.

When the gorgeous dinner was over and the guests had left, the *cadi* continued to ponder how the evil spirits had been able to make him their plaything to such a degree, projecting to his mortal eyes such wild false images. At that moment his wife stepped in front of him, bowed deeply, and said:

'Master, I beg for your forgiveness. It is not that Allah has empowered Those Others to blur your clear thinking. It was I who just wanted to demonstrate to you how a woman can cleverly fool a man, even if he be a *cadi*.'

Now the *cadi* understood his wife's wisdom. From that day, no woman ever succeeded in influencing him with sighs and tears. They were no longer pronounced right when they did not deserve it.

El hamdulillah! Praise be to God.

THE SEVENTH WIFE

(1932)

FADILA

News of the wedding of this girl of twelve reached me at the home of Lalla Zohra as we were drinking the traditional mint tea. I was on one of those low sitting mattresses lining the walls and turning the long, narrow Moroccan room into a single comfortable sofa under a rather high ceiling. The attentive hostess had heaped behind my back a whole pile of cushions, some of them in rectangular velvet pillowcases packed hard with sheep wool and others in small round muslin covers. Sitting cross-legged in the oriental fashion for a long time proved extremely tiring for someone from Europe, so when the servant girl left, I relaxed and stretched my legs out on the rug. There was no longer any risk of her tripping over my feet with her steaming brass kettle, from which from time to time she added water to the teapot.

Lalla Zohra, who was small and thin, sat facing me, cross-legged in her ample green gown. The conversation waned as the dusk slid into the room. Lalla Zohra seemed to fall into deep thought. The shrill calls of the swallows could be heard from outside; at sunset in Marrakech, these birds always cruised in dense flocks. Downstairs the servant was hustling around in the patio, clanking her buckets and humming. The spirals of the window grid made a sharp silhouette against the background of a yellowish evening sky. The window faced an off-white house wall with a similar small gridded window.

The house of Lalla Zohra's husband was no different from all others in the city: one of those lidless clay boxes in which the Moroccan man hides his women and his home life. It is a rectangular well of two storeys, with all windows directed on to the internal patio.

Shadows were rapidly filling the room. Suddenly Lalla Zohra announced:

68

'Ben Ahmed is going to marry. He'll marry Fadila, Lalla Zubida's cousin. You know Ahmed, don't you?'

I certainly did — a tall, young and wealthy merchant with gold eye-teeth, who drove his own car — but I knew Lalla Zubida even better. She was the first Moroccan woman I had known, a simple young wife of innate intelligence who had become my friend. But I did not know Fadila, or even her family.

'How old is she?'

'Fadila is twelve. Ahmed is about thirty. But you know, he paid seven and a half thousand francs for the girl. Of course, for someone like him that is not a large sum.'

'Has Ben Ahmed seen Fadila?' I could not help asking such a silly question. It so rarely occurred that a suitor saw his future wife before the wedding night, but still . . . Ben Ahmed had modern views.

'He hasn't.' Lalla Zohra laughed: 'They are an odd couple. Part of the groom should be chopped off and added to the bride.' But then her voice betrayed concern: 'Fadila will be the seventh woman Ben Ahmed has married. He divorced the first six. He changes wives fast. His latest one was Bentshinbou, a *chikha* known all over the town. You must have heard of this professional dancer.' Lalla Zohra laughed again, but this time in a peculiar way: 'Well, I am myself a seventh wife. Over the twenty years before my time, Sidi Moktar married four maidens and two women who had been married before. With the first one he had a daughter, who died. But he has been married with me for a full eleven years.'

In the darkness I could not see Lalla Zohra's face, but her words indicated contentment. She had presented Sidi Moktar with four sons; Allah had recalled two, but the two others had survived. Sidi Moktar would never divorce the mother of his sons.

INVITATION

It must have been entered into my Book of Fate that, as the sole Christian among orthodox Muslims, I was to partake in the wedding celebration of a complete stranger, an Arab woman called Fadila.

The invitation was brought by Lalla Zubida, wrapped in her white *haik* and carefully veiled. She explained with an air of importance that the wedding would take place in her house, since she was a close relative of the bride whose parents' house was too small for such a great occasion. I wondered why the feast was not going to take place in the groom's sumptuous house. That would come anyway, but later, she said. Why so? Very simple: at first the bride's parents with their relatives and friends would celebrate their daughter's leaving the house, while Ben Ahmed would spend his last days as a bachelor in the convivial company of his friends. Thus the celebration would start simultaneously at the bride's and at the groom's house. When Fadila was taken to the groom's home on the wedding night, new feasting would start there.

'How long will the celebrations last?'

'Not less than seven days.'

'And when and where should I come?'

Lalla Zubida bowed to me ceremoniously, pressing her hand against her chest: 'Fadila's parents send the *tbib* and you their greetings. Allah's blessing be with both of you. Let both of you come to my house Thursday at noon.' She reassumed her everyday style: 'It's true this is the men's day. But in your case, she added somewhat apologetically, 'it hardly matters.' 'The men's day?'

'Well, yes. As you know, women cannot expose themselves to the gaze of male strangers, so they meet separately on Friday. But you can come on Thursday as well, since you are a *roumia*, a Christian woman.'

MEN'S DAY

On Thursday the sun was shining almost exactly on the tops of our heads as we walked to the wedding house, not far from the Djemaa el-Fna square where the noonday heat had thinned out the crowds. The open-air performances had not yet begun. The snake-charmers, acrobats and magicians were in the cool of their homes; vendors were dozing behind their stacks of pots and piles of oranges, peering at us sleepily from under their turbans, which they had pulled down over their eyes.

Heading from the square into the souks, we only had to walk a few dozen yards through the bazaar under its roof made of reeds, before turning into *derb* Znaktarahba. This narrow side street was probably one of the most animated places in Marrakech. Dust, raised by humans, donkeys and camels treading the unpaved earth, mixed with tiny flecks of straw and hung between the walls as a reddish haze. One of the walls contained the door, covered in sheet-iron and only five feet high, of Lalla Zubida's house.

We hardly had time to rattle the iron ring before a boy shouted at the top of his voice *'Ashkoun?'* (Who is it?), and Zubida's half-brother Abdallah opened the door. We knew we were expected, since he did not rush off to announce us but seized our hands and started guiding us through the sombre passage that led to the central patio.

'Be careful not to trip up,' he said. 'Here are some steps — one, two . . . careful! One, two, three . . . We have so many people here . . . one more step . . . and musicians.' The spacious cemented patio was gleamingly clean. Rugs hung on the surrounding walls, their colour adding to the verve of a festive occasion, and another rug was spread in the middle of the patio for the musicians. Each of the four walls had a tall double door, and the bride's father came dashing out of one of these — a lean middle-aged man, thin-lipped and with a sparse beard. He wore a brown *djellaba*. At the threshold he retrieved his slippers and put them on, then hurried forward to meet us. He was followed more leisurely by Lalla Zubida's husband, a rather swarthy man with a Turkish hat made of white felt. He had regular features on which a perpetual smile seemed to play.

After thorough greetings, reciprocal bows, and invoking Allah's blessings, we were led into one of the rooms. The *tbib* and I sat on the mattresses and found that we were the only visitors in this chamber. The male relatives and family friends seemed to be congregated in the room from which the master of the feast had come out a little time before. It hummed with voices and by the threshhold were a good number of yellow slippers. Soon we were holding those fragrant glasses of sticky sweet mint tea. After once more wishing us all the earthly goods conceivable, the bride's father left the room, leaving only Lalla Zubida's husband.

The musicians started playing, cross-legged and holding a violin vertically on the knees. There were five of them, all middle-aged. One was blind, and he abandoned himself to the music, transported by the rather hoarse sounds produced by the rounded violin bow. The drummer inclined his head, wobbled his body, and tilted his large thundering drum like a sowing tray. The youngest man pressed a *derbouka* under his arm — a small hour-glass-shaped clay drum. Above the rhythm sounded the clatter of a tambourine.

Where, I wondered, was the bride? I looked up towards the gridded upper-floor windows. Was she observing her own marriage festivities? One more day, and she would be living in a strange house belonging to a man she had never seen before. A female figure slipped into the room, her head and shoulders wrapped in a kerchief. Lalla Zubida's face emerged. She laughed and greeted the *tbib* and me.

'Oh, today there are men everywhere in the house. It's difficult even to move around.'

'You must have a lot of work on your hands. I feel sorry for you.'

She made a comic face and waved her hand in the air so that all her silver and gold bracelets tinkled:

'The whole house is upside down! I only slept a few hours.' I immediately got to the most intriguing point: 'How is the *laroussa*, the bride? Can one go and greet her?' Lalla Zubida looked at me in astonishment, as if I had mentioned someone completely irrelevant to the situation. Her eyes seemed to say that only foreigners could make such requests. But, all the same, she nodded. 'Come along,' she said, wrapping herself again in the kerchief. 'I'll take you to the *laroussa*.' I followed her. A spiral staircase close by took us to the second floor and the balcony which today was in use as a kitchen. About ten older women squatted on the floor next to a maze of pots, chafing dishes, basins, pies, and roast chickens. Veiny arms were raised toward me: *Marhabbik!* Welcome! How are you?' 'So-so, not so bad,' I responded in the required way, shaking the women's hands and then kissing my right index finger. 'So you want to see the bride? Well, she is right here, our little dove, our pomegranate blossom.' Only now did I notice the little bundle huddled against the wall. Cautiously I lifted the hem of the grey cloth covering her. A young girl, no — I should rather say a child — sat cross-legged with head lowered. Her not exactly beautiful face was pale, with eyelids swollen as if she had just been crying. Tasty morsels were heaped in front of her: chicken wings, honeycakes, almonds. But the *laroussa*'s hands rested in her lap, the palms turned upwards. The delicacies were untouched.

Why did I suddenly recall a picture from the past: the door of the physician's consulting room in our home opened and a tall young man wearing a Turkish hat and a light blue bournous stepped out. He had dark glasses, and he flung the flap of his bournous over his shoulder with a sharp movement as he approached the stairs. It was Ben Ahmed, the bridegroom . . . Would his seventh wife find grace in his eyes? Would Fadila conquer the heart of that man?

I pronounced the customary greeting: May Allah bestow health on you! Fadila slowly raised her head and cast a shy glance at me. She was cross-eyed. My need to say something positive and encouraging to her was almost a physical one. I groped for words. 'Ben Ahmed is a handsome man. You will be happy.'

'Allah!' the old women joined me in a comforting chorus. 'You will be happy. We all have gone through it. We were merry. But today you must nonetheless weep as much as you can. This is every bride's duty, and it brings good luck later in life.' 'Let's go and eat now,' Lalla Zubida said to me. As we descended to the patio she touched my arm and asked:

'Do you want to see the bride's mother? She's right here.'

Both parts of the double door leading to the room next to the stairs were closed. One entered through a smaller door, barely the height of a man, built into the larger door — a frequent feature in

the Moorish building style. A multi-coloured cloth covered the
door opening. The small, high-ceilinged room had plastered walls,
and the whole floor was covered with trays and flat dishes heaped
full of cakes and biscuits: dark brown 'stork's nests' dripping with
honey, 'gazelle horns' with almond filling, and pies made of puff
pastry. In the middle of this fragrant pile gleaming with oil, a
light-skinned woman, still quite young, sat cross-legged in front
of a sizzling chafing dish on which she cooked these sweetmeats.
A firm line round her mouth and a penetrating glance indicated
vigour.

This was Lalla Habiba, the bride's mother. We exchanged
greetings, and she told me to follow Lalla Zubida into another
room where the *tbib* already sat. The feast now began at once. We
gathered around the circular foot-high table and washed our
hands.

The most important dish was served first: *bastila*, a delicate
meat pie round and large like the table on which it stood. The
mystery of its contents was solved only by digging a narrow
furrow with one's fingers, which one then allowed to deviate
neither to left nor right, boring towards the pie's centre. The thin
crust broke under the probing fingers and crumbled with a slight
crackle into layers thin as tissue paper, exposing a sweet almond
filling. Then the fingers dipped unexpectedly into onion puree,
and then one's way was blocked by the tiny wing of a dove, and
then successively bits of egg, chicken liver, legs of doves and
chickens, and more almond filling. The sweet and the salty combined with spices made *bastila* extraordinarily delicious — the
greatest achievement of the Arab culinary art.

The *bastila* was followed by chicken without which even the
most spare of feasts would be unthinkable. Preparing chicken with
various mixtures to yield countless nuances of taste is a Moroccan
specialty. This time three differently prepared chickens, all fried
till they reached the right golden brown, were served together: one
with olives, one with marinated lemon peel, and one with saffron.

It would be impossible to end such a feast with the stomach
only moderately full. The chicken was followed by two *tajines* or
stews: first cinnamon-flavoured mutton with the inevitable

sugared onions, and then beef with beans. Hot fat crackled as the *tajine* dishes were heaved in front of us. In contrast to the *bastila*, one had to proceed cautiously, starting with the vegetables at the surface. If one's curious fingers tried to burrow into the interior of the dish, they would have to be withdrawn in a flash — such was the heat.

During the whole feast the musicians played without stopping — their music was like arabesques, with the sound sliding, intertwining and separating again, never delaying and never forming melodic elements of the kind familiar to Europeans.

When the spit-roasted lamb appeared, accompanied by small dishes of spices, the musicians added song to the instrumental music. The rhythm steadily grew faster and more ardent. The singing rang loud and shrill, with vigorous instrumental support. Then suddenly there was silence. The music seemed to have stopped in the middle of a phrase. The players sat, looking indifferent as if they had never had anything to do with music. You could have heard a pin drop.

Everyone knew that this was the climax of the feast. It ended with tea. Lalla Habiba's cakes were heaped in front of us in a huge pile, that somehow reminded one of the European folktale of having to eat a passage through a mountain of sweet things in order to reach home. Abdallah, the boy who had opened the door to us, had been sitting on the rug at our feet, having wrapped himself in his white tunic.

'The musicians will soon be leaving now, and the feast will be over,' he said plaintively, and the small tuft of hair left unshaven at the top of his head quivered.

ON FRIDAY

It was three o'clock when I hurried toward Lalla Zubida's home, this time alone. As on the day before, I rattled the iron ring at the door and groped through the half-dark hallway. Lalla Zubida and the bride's mother came across the deserted patio to meet me.

'Why have you come so late?' they asked. 'All the other guests

have been here since morning.' I was taken to the room where the
men had had their feast the day before. Five or six women were
stretched out at full length on the sitting mattresses along the
wall. My entrance disturbed their sleep, and they slowly sat up,
yawning. One of them, fat as a barrel, puffed as she propped
herself up and seemed to speak for the rest of them: 'Ah! It's you,
tbiba. How are you? Come and sit here.' She pulled me to her side.
'Why didn't you come earlier? We have already eaten.'

The word 'eaten' explained their slumber. Which one of us
would not have felt exhausted after such an enormous and over-
nourishing meal? European etiquette does not apply in Morocco.
If the honoured guests feel their eyelids becoming heavy, they are
welcome to lie down, arrange a pillow, and sleep. May Allah bless
their digestion! Thus the siesta indicated that the celebrations
were in full swing.

My round-eyed neighbour inspected me from top to toe, and
there followed a number of questions. In contrast to the rest, who
quietly arranged their clothes and assumed a dignified sitting
position in line with Arab good breeding, the fat matron wanted
to know why I wore a hat and what I had in my purse. Her
questions became more and more intimate. Her flabby face was
thick with make-up, and when she laughed one saw that her
tongue and gums were parched brown with walnut-tree bark. A
black line drawn with kohl on the inner edge of her brows gave
her an insistent look.

The other women also used make-up, but more moderately.
Everyone was festively attired. Pink, green and yellow broadcloth
caftans were covered with silk and muslin dfinas or gowns. Wide
gold- or silver-embroidered leather belts had large gold or silver
buckles decorated with red gems. Colourful silken kerchiefs
exposed the forehead with the glittering metboua, a round ornament with pendants. One young and very beautiful woman in
particular was richly adorned and seemed to belong to a wealthier
class.

As on the day before, I was concerned to know where the bride
was to be found. Now that there were only women in the whole
house, would she still be sitting on the balcony? I asked bluntly:

'Where is the *laroussa*?'

There was no answer, but everyone's glance turned towards an embroidered lace curtain in an isolated corner. Was that where the *laroussa* was hidden? Encouraged by a hand gesture, I rose and peered behind the embroidery. Fadila was huddled up on a mattress. I only saw the back of her gold-stitched velvet gown. Isolated tufts of her henna-dyed copper-red hair fell on her shoulders. The girl was pressing her face against the wall.

'Fadila!' I called out to her. Mutely she turned her head. Without raising her eyes she offered her hand. I held it in my palm: it was now decorated with an intricate design. The thin henna script, reddish brown as if drawn with iodine, covered everything like a glove. Her finger tips and nails were fully dyed brown. Yes, during the night the bride had undergone the henna procedure. An old woman proficient in the art had been invited, and by candlelight she had applied the henna patterns to the bride's hands and feet. Patiently she had dried her handiwork till dawn over a chafing dish, careful to avoid touching the hands and legs that were sticky with the henna mush so as not to blur the design. The end-result was a delicate and graceful lace pattern.

'Why is Fadila segregated from the others?' I inquired.

'Why, she's a mere girl! Let her get married — then she'll be entitled to sit with us wives. Furthermore, she must be sheltered from the evil eye,' the fat lady said. She went to the bride, sat beside her, and patted her on the shoulder.

'Oh, little daughter, are you already craving for the entrance of Ben Ahmed?' She laughed out loud. 'Believe me: your heart will soon leap with joy like a gazelle in the desert.'

The bride's head sank still lower so that the white nape of her neck could be seen between the tufts of hair. But the fat lady did not bother with the *laroussa*'s feelings and continued in the same immodest vein. I looked towards the other guests: how were they reacting? They sat motionless, without smiling, and with demure eyes. Probably it was customary to cheer up the bride with such talk. And Fadila had cause to be cheerful. Fate had not assigned her a groom in his seventies, but rather a young and attractive one.

I returned to my earlier seat facing the open door. Meanwhile, more women had appeared in the patio. They must have been slumbering in other rooms. The number grew steadily until several dozen of them were congregated in the open space. They stood around conversing, carrying odd bundles of clothing, and ambled across the yard from one room to the other, dragging their heelless slippers. Lalla Zohra whisked by in a pink caftan. Some removed their kerchiefs and rearranged their hair. My companions, too, left the room.

I was left alone and after a while began to feel conspicuous and out of place. Were they preparing to go home? Had the wedding feast ended? Just as I had made up my mind to get up and say good-bye, the beautiful young matron whose adornments had particularly caught my attention returned, followed by an old black woman with a bundle of clothes. Without a word the young wife seized the silk shawl from my shoulders. She smiled comfortingly at my puzzlement, pulled her heavy-fringed shawl from her head, and dropped it in my lap: 'Here, take mine!' And since I did not know what to do with it, the servant tied it at my head in such a way that the parting of the hair could be seen and the fringe fell on the shoulders. The matron opened the bundle, taking out a still more elaborate caftan and a gayer *dfina* than the ones she was wearing. With the servant's help she changed clothes. Did she intend to cover her head with my shawl? O, unobtrusive European shawl! Despite your contemporary stylishness, who would have cared about you in that country of flaming colors? a sparkling brocade scarf was pulled from the bundle and tied at her head. Then they both walked out, leaving me alone again.

They were preparing for something to happen — but what? Where was Lalla Zubida whom I could ask? I would hardly be able to find her, since she had so much to do and manage. Would she be on the upper floor? Holding my neck stiff because of the shawl's tendency to slip off, I stumbled up the steep stairs and found her indeed. Squatting, she held a small glass to Lalla Zohra who was powdering herself. The two friends concentrated on making up as if it were a sacred rite. Lalla Zohra no longer had her pink caftan but a light blue one delicately covered with a white silk *dfina*. Add the gold jewellery, and she was like a princess.

Lalla Zubida nodded to me: 'Wait a little. You will be given other clothes too. Too bad you don't have any jewellery. Now it's too late to go and borrow them from the Jew. We all borrow them. The *laroussa* included. But now go downstairs.' What else was there for me to do but retrace my path and sit and wait on the sofa. It did not take long before the black woman returned carrying on her arm a yellow caftan and white *dfina* with yellow flowers.

'Get up!' she ordered.

When I was on my feet, a wide-sleeved floor-length caftan was thrown over my European-style dress. The Moroccan caftan has its buttons in front like a coat, but there are forty or fifty of those pea-sized buttons formed from the curls of an ornamental cord, running down the length of the caftan. Braid and patterns made of decorative cord further adorned my broadcloth caftan. The *dfina* was sewn to fit the caftan. Its skirt portion had three loosely-falling flaps allowing the caftan to be seen, and forming with it a harmony of colours. This mass of stuffs was held together with a leather belt stitched with yellow silk.

'Holy Sidi Larbi!' the old negress fretted, trying to fix the buckle. 'How slim you are! Why don't you eat more? It doesn't look pretty when a woman isn't stout.' Silently, I accepted the reproof. She was right: two people of my size would have fitted inside that belt. I cast a furtive glance towards the patio. Where could this fleshy woman be whose clothes I had been given and to whom I so sadly failed to measure up? I did not feel comfortable in those garments.

As I crossed the threshold to the patio, the clanking of the iron ring at the outer door reverberated throughout the house. '*Ashkoun?* Who is it?' A few minutes later four figures, seeming like bunches of white blankets, emerged from the tunnel of the vestibule. Hidden in the folds of their *haiks*, they carried musical instruments which they now set on the floor. They dropped the *haiks* near the wall and plucked the scarves from their faces. Four *chikhas* were at the disposal of the patrons.

But how could a Moroccan dancing girl start her work without drinking mint tea? All four of them were soon squatting around a tray, while the ladies of the house and their servants laid out the rugs in the patio. The long sitting mattresses were dragged out from the rooms to enclose the carpeted area, and the guests immediately occupied them. In no time the women had formed themselves into what looked like a motley wreath, so densely packed that there wasn't a single spot left for me. The group had by now become amazingly large, maybe as many as thirty. I finally found a vacant spot at the threshold of the room where the bride was, and those close by courteously helped me to slip through.

All the women sitting there had exchanged their earlier festive gowns for ones that were more festive still. Their faces, so carefully made up, were dead-serious. A few vigorous beats on the *derbouka* drum gave the *chikhas* the signal. The tambourine began to chirp. One of the singers started on a high note with the introductory 'In the name of the graceful and merciful Allah!' She drew the words out, swooped to a lower pitch, then leapt high again, and ended suddenly on a screechingly high note. The other singers joined in, accompanied by the droning and jangling music. The song first gave thanks to Allah, then developed into a praise for the household, and finally into a love song.

Two of the *chikhas* were past middle age, their halcyon days long past. One of them, snub-nosed and apathetic, seemed to be the troop leader. The red cheeks of the other reminded me irresistibly of Estonian farm women. Full of vivacity and humour, she smacked her lips as she played, winked suggestively, shook her shoulders, and burst into guffaws when the comments of her companions reached her ears. Some youthful freshness of voice was injected into the quartet by a pretty girl of about eighteen. The fourth *chikha* was tall and thin, with two protruding yellow teeth.

The *chikhas* rested — they sipped tea, lit cigarettes, and warmed the *derbouka* skins over a chafing dish. The guests sat quietly, without exchanging a word. Some furtively slipped their hands inside their belt as if looking for something. Suddenly the oldest *chikha* stood in front of me.

'It is inadmissible to attend a wedding feast without make-up. Allow me to beautify you.' As fast as lightning, she produced a lipstick from her bosom, licked it over, and lay a thick red layer on my mouth.

There are moments in life where one's mouth drops open out of surprise — mine did so then, not just out of astonishment but revulsion also. While looking for my handkerchief I glanced at those around me: grave nods approved of the *chikha*'s act. To wipe off the lipstick would be an open insult to the bride, so I pursed my lips and sat still.

Singing began anew. The most gaunt of the *chikhas* stepped into the middle of the circle, holding a narrow scarf in front of her. She slung it around her neck, arched herself, and threw her head back. She dreamily scanned the audience with half-closed eyes, her lips drew into a smile, her foot beat the ground, and she started a kind of a heel-and-toe dance step. Suddenly her body seemed to become two separate parts with lives of their own. The upper part became rigid, while the lower shook from the rapid movement of the feet. The soles pattered incessantly in one place, at times appearing to bounce up as if from a trampoline. The skirt tail suddenly began to float, to crinkle, and finally to undulate smoothly. Within this whirl the dancer herself seemed passive and motionless.

The feet stopped with a thump. Skirt waves rose high, crossed, and dissipated into a mere wrinkled hem. The dancer stepped in front of the bride's mother, and now her broad belt went into motion. Lifted by the belly, it rose to just under the breasts before falling back. Then again it rose, with the belly describing circles — once, twice, and a third time. The *chikha* turned her back to Lalla Habiba, and now her buttocks rose and fell in a circle, also three times. Some more patter with the feet, and the *chikha* sank on one knee and extended her palm toward the bride's mother. Slowly and with dignity, Lalla Habiba stuck her finger tips within her belt, produced a crisp new five-franc note, and placed it in the open palm from where the dancing girl whisked it to her bosom.

The same dance was repeated in front of every woman: three belly circles, three buttock circles, some foot pattering and, going down on one knee, the suddenly ungainly *chikha* would seize her five francs.

'Take it!' the women's somewhat disdainful air seemed to

convey. 'Take the money and show us your art — to us virtuous wives who are not like you.'

And the *chikha* seemed to reply ironically: 'OK, I'll dance for you in honour of the bride and my own sake, to earn money. But don't you forget, little sisters, that I also have more passionate dances with which I can seduce your husbands . . .'

Now it was my turn to be danced to. A faint smile spread to all faces and even about the *chikha*'s lips a look of benevolence appeared. To dance for a Christian! What a joke! My waist was adorned with a broad and thick belt, and behind it was enough space for a whole sack of money, but alas! there was only yawning emptiness. Where could I find a five-franc note? Lalla Zubida rushed to my rescue.

'Take these. . . . This is from the *tbiba*!' she called to the dancing girl as she dropped a few coins into her palm. When the *chikha* started to inspect them, Lalla Zubida added sternly:

'That's plenty for you! The *tbiba* is a *roumia*. She came to the wedding without knowing our customs. Get on with your dance!'

A few more rounds for the remaining guests, and the *chikha* returned to the wall. Her fingers rattled the *derbouka*, and her rusty voice joined in with the song of her companions.

MISHAP

It is imprudent to invite a Christian to a wedding. The *djnun*, the spirits of the house whom one may never trust, can be dangerous for the bride. They can be held at bay with the word of God, but how would a Christian be able to deter their insidious schemes when he or she does not practise fasting and obeys none of the other commands of Islam?

While the singing and dancing went on, twilight had descended on the patio. The square patch of sky above was still blue, but with a tint that announced nightfall. White shapes shimmered above the roof edges: the women of neighbouring houses, attracted by the music, were joining in the celebration in their own way.

Even as the dancing continued, some of the bride's relatives had slipped past me to her room. Now Lalla Habiba went there too. The disappearance of the bride's mother behind the curtain at her daughter's door turned the company oddly restless. Suspense filled the air.

Suddenly the patio rang from shrill deafening screams: *yu-yu-yu!* This metallic-sounding whoop is produced by a rapid tongue oscillation from one corner of the mouth to the other. Not everyone can acquire the particular skill necessary to produce it, but every house has some practitioners. Here, too, it was indispensable for triggering the climax of the celebration.

Three women simultaneously rushed out from behind the curtain and made their way between me and my neighbour, carrying lighted candles in tall brass candelabra. The curtain was pushed aside, and four women came out carrying a large round brass tray on their heads. The *laroussa* was sitting on it. They headed towards the patio.

And then it happened as fate had foreseen. Right as she passed me, one of the carriers stumbled and lost her balance. The tray tilted threateningly above my head. The bride's hands clasped convulsively at the rim of the tray. She was going to fall. . . . For a second we all held our breath. Then the stumbler righted herself — the *laroussa* was saved. How could I have suspected the momentousness of the event — that stumbling at a Christian forbode ill for the bride?

The *laroussa* reached the centre of the circle of seated women. The *yu-yu-yu* gathered new strength. My eyes focused on Fadila, squatting cross-legged on the tray, completely covered by an airy kerchief. Lalla Habiba stepped proudly up to her daughter, and with a majestic gesture pointed to the gorgeous golden crown she wore — to which the audience responded with an appreciative *yu-yu-yu*. Next, the mother pointed to a nearly hand-sized golden charm with a red stone pendant her daughter wore on her chest; a stormy *yu-yu* resounded again. None of the bride's ornaments was missed: thick gold bracelets on both wrists, the row of rings on her fingers, the French *louis d'or* at each ear. And so that the guests might appreciate this splendour better the carriers rotated the bride three times in the candle light.

Fadila kept her eyelids lowered and looked lifeless. She was carried back to her room. The last day of her maiden life was about to end. Only a few preparations remained, and then before dawn Ben Ahmed's car would stop at the door. The moment Fadila entered the car her life would be torn into two parts. The first part — her carefree childhood — would be irretrievably gone.

We sat silently in the twilight. Were the women's thoughts delving into their own past history? Did they remember the day when they had sat on the tray? Fate had allocated to each person her particular role.

Candles were lit in the patio. The guests rose. Night was at hand. It was time to go home! The master and the household were waiting there. Some further *tajines* were carried into the open space, and we gathered round them without delay. Steam arose from the earthen basins. We ate hurriedly. Candles flickered, casting reflections from the ornaments on to the women's arms, heads and chests. We ourselves remained in the shadow: only the gold seemed to live.

I slipped in alone to bid the *laroussa* farewell. The room was dark. The light of the candles in the patio dimly illuminated Fadila. All ornaments — her own and those borrowed from the Jew — had been removed. The bride was curled against the wall, asleep. She slept the all-forgetting sleep of youth.

FIRST MONTHS OF MARRIAGE

The morning after the wedding night, servants brought the young wife a breakfast cooked by her mother. Lalla Habiba herself could enter her son-in-law's house only three days later, and when she did she took several *tajines* with her. She was allowed to stay there till the end of the wedding celebrations — the evening of the seventh day. At that point all women had to leave Ben Ahmed's house: his mother, aunts, friends and female relatives.

How did Fadila feel in her new home? From time to time I heard news of her from Lalla Zubida, who as a neutral person was allowed to visit Fadila a couple of times. The young wife was bored, she said. The house was certainly nice and large, but there was apparently mistrust between her and the servants. After all, they had already seen six wives before her come and go! For the time being she could not offer her help in the kitchen: that would have been against custom.

Ben Ahmed was seldom at home. When he did return, he often brought friends with him, and then the young mistress of the house had to flee to its farthest recesses to escape the men's glances.

In times long gone by, Ben Ahmed's father had bought a female slave from the Sudan, and as this woman had got older she gained command of the household. It was she who gave orders to the servants and kept an eye on the young wife. Fadila did not trust her; in spite of an insipidly sweet manner, she immediately realised that the old black woman considered her a nobody. Hadn't Fadila by chance overheard a whispered conversation between the black woman and a servant sent to her by Bentshinbou, the *chikha*? When she heard how young Fadila was, hadn't Bentshinbou made plans to resume her old place in Ben Ahmed's house?

Fadila appreciated the visits she received from Lalla Zubida. It was so heartening to see her older friend's good-natured, perennially smiling face, and through her Fadila heard news of her former home. She brought with her something of what had been Fadila's past. Ah, one could envy Lalla Zubida — her husband allowed her so much freedom. She had even been to the movies, and had sat with the *tbib* in the Christian café where they played such strange music. Yes, Lalla Zubida was clever and bold.

Just over a month had passed since the wedding when Fadila's mother became critically ill. I heard of it through Lalla Zubida, and went to see her, as elementary politeness dictated. Poor Lalla! There she lay, surrounded by sobbing women, whose diffused lament was pierced by her cries of pain: 'Sidi Larbi! Holy Sidi Larbi, hear me!' Special smoke to deter evil spirits pervaded the room.

'*Allah akbar!* God is the highest of all,' the other women said to comfort the sufferer, and kissed her hands and sweaty brow. My eyes sought Fadila, but she was not there.

'It's too early for Lalla Fadila to leave her husband's house,' Lalla Zubida whispered. 'She hasn't even been to the baths yet for the ablution ritual — so how could she come here? Do you see that old black woman at the other end of the room? That's the one who runs Ben Ahmed's household and watches over Fadila. She is here in place of the young wife.'

How ugly she was. Sensing that we were talking about her, she bared her teeth in a smile. Her snub-nosed face had something malicious about it indeed. Lalla Zubida once more brought her lips to my ear:

'You know, Fadila is pregnant! D'you realise?' No, I did not quite realise.

Fadila's mother recovered from her sickness. At our next encounter with Lalla Zubida I did not fail to ask after the health of the newly-wed wife.

'She's no longer pregnant,' was the brief answer. 'They secretly had her drink some drugs.' I recalled the link between the black woman and Bentshinbou, the *chikha*.

When two months had passed since the wedding the young wife was allowed to leave her husband's house for the first time, and accompanied by the black woman she paid the obligatory formal visit to her parental home. Fadila was no longer that small girl who would run barefoot to the store, a piece of calico thrown over her face and shoulders, to buy mint or candles for her mother. As Ben Ahmed's wife she was escorted by a servant and walked at a measured step in high-soled embroidered slippers, an embroidered kerchief covering all of her face above and below the eyes. Her *haik* was as white as snow, and she used both hands to keep it somewhat off her face to see her step.

Meeting the family was refreshing. Her mother and aunts could finally ask her the most burning questions.

'Have you menstruated?'

'No, I haven't.'

So Fadila was pregnant, after all — indisputably pregnant. The secretly brewed herbs had proved ineffectual.

'*El hamdulillah!* Praise be to Allah!'

REVERSAL

Another month went by. On the surface Fadila's life looked satisfactory, but then something completely unexpected and crazy happened: Ben Ahmed returned Fadila to her parents' home! He cast his wife out, as they say. The marriage contract remained in force.

Might this man take Fadila back? Did he perhaps intend to contract other marriages meanwhile? Who could answer such questions?

The angry father was in a fury: who dared to offer such an insult to a respected citizen like himself! Who and what was that Ben Ahmed, after all? Of course, he himself would have gone sooner or later to retrieve his daughter. He had come to realise a long time since that Ben Ahmed, despite his wealth, was an unfit match for Fadila. He lacked good sense: wasn't he even known sometimes to drink French anisette, in contravention of the holy command against alcohol? Only such a half-wit could repudiate a wife who was with child!

That Fadila was pregnant was an article of faith to her mother, and all their relatives joined her in that certainty. Who had so beclouded Ben Ahmed's sound judgment as to make him commit that unheard-of deed: casting off a wife who was going to bear his son?

Having thought the situation out, Fadila's father saw another possibility: perhaps Ben Ahmed did not even know of his wife's pregnancy! Given Fadila's self-effacing character and the modesty that went with her extreme youth, this was surely possible. This had to be the answer: the husband didn't know. His wife's pregnancy had to be announced to Ben Ahmed through the female grapevine. Because he had not succeeded in getting an heir out of six wives, he would want Fadila back at any cost when he heard about her condition. But the father would not be so dumb as to yield to that; let the wealthy Ben Ahmed first pay a good sum in compensation. When the child was born, the *cadi* would settle the matter, and Fadila, in full glory, would resume her role in running Ben Ahmed's household.

Meanwhile Fadila's life continued between the four walls of her parents' home, and to outsiders it appeared calm. Day followed day with the usual chores, as before. It was just that a new dwelling was rented, bigger and handsomer than the previous one. Custom demanded that the young wife should have a room of her own, and the more spacious house was also in line with the family's new standing. A son would be born, a name-giving ceremony would be held, and it was so cumbersome to have all the celebrations at someone else's home. That it would be a boy they all took for granted.

Fadila's looks had meanwhile changed appreciably, and for the better. She was still pale, and still slightly cross-eyed under those heavy lids, but her childish expression had become more mature and intelligent. She now had more curves, and her arms and legs had become fuller; yet her attitude remained the same. She was sparing of words in the presence of visitors, and sat upright in their midst, hands in her lap and eyes downcast, although she seemed to follow the conversation closely. When I happened to address her, she would tilt her head and smile shyly, which gave her face a charmingly soft expression. But she preferred to keep busy with chores. Her bare legs would move in even steps over the tiles of the patio. With the caftan tail stuck into her belt, her legs could move more freely and her knee-long bag trousers were exposed. The rolled-up gown also made her hips appear wider, and a striped scarf serving as an apron further added volume. What did she herself think of this whole affair? No one bothered to ask her.

Time passed. One afternoon Lalla Zubida was again visiting me. We sat and looked out the window — these gridless European windows appealed to her. My visitor's face sank in the sparse curtain behind which the Djemaa el-Fna plaza buzzed and seethed. Suddenly she exclaimed, pointing at a man in a light blue burnous riding a bicycle:

'Look! There is Ben Ahmed, Fadila's husband. Just think of it: he has already found another wife.'

'When did he marry?'

'They say he went to the *cadi* for the marriage contract three days ago. And you know whom he took back? Bentshinbou!'

'Does Fadila know? What does she say?'

'Oh, she cannot be happy. You know, Ben Ahmed has repeatedly sent Rahalia, that inveterate gossip, to Fadila's father with gifts and pleas to return her. Only last week he sent the message: "Why do you refuse to let your daughter return? Am I not wealthy enough? Can't I feed a wife and child?" The father's stubborn answer was: "You are wanting in good sense, and because of that Fadila will stay in my house until the birth of her child." '

'But now that Ben Ahmed has married the *chikha*,' Lalla Zubida resumed, 'Fadila's return is not so simple any longer. Such a *chikha* you know, she has no family background; she is like. . . .' Lalla Zubida's hand made the motion of throwing something up towards the ceiling: 'She's nothing at all, you know. Fadila is young and naive, and an experienced *chikha* could well seize the reins of the household, and even get Fadila out of the way for good. But of course the birth is no longer far off — a mere two months — and then Fadila will be basking in everyone's good opinions.'

WHEN THE EMBRYO TAKES A NAP

It was the eighth month of Lalla Fadila's pregnancy. In another few weeks, the child would arrive.

One morning three women wrapped in *haiks* were standing at the *tbib*'s door. As they lowered their veils in his waiting room, well-known faces emerged: an anxious Lalla Habiba, a calm Lalla Zubida, and a bashful Lalla Fadila. What had happened? It did not look good. The waters had broken the previous evening, and a premature birth might take place at any time. The *tbib*'s help was needed.

The physician examined the patient. He turned serious, shook his head, and asked the mother to come in from the waiting-room. And then those horrible words bored into Lalla Habiba's ears:

'There is no child!'

Thunder-struck, Fadila's mother leaped from her chair: 'What?'

'There just is no child. There never was. Fadila is still too young.'

For a moment Lalla Habiba just stood staring. Then, seeming calmer, she sat down again. Had they come all this way just to hear such idle talk? The mother sighed and turned again to the *tbib*:

'All right, have another look — a better look — and tell us whether she will give birth today or whether it will take longer.'

Before the *tbib* could answer, Fadila interrupted in a clear voice: 'It seems I haven't got a child.'

This was too much for Lalla Habiba, who jumped up again, grabbed her veil, tied it to her face, and pulled the *haik* over her head.

'Come!' she ordered her daughter. 'Get Lalla Zubida from the other room. We're leaving.'

Lalla Zubida was benumbed by the physician's diagnosis. Helplessly, she looked from Lalla Habiba to the *tbib* and then to Fadila. Lalla Habiba did not leave her time to think. 'We are leaving,' she repeated and made for the door. Dazed, the others followed her.

When they reached home, Lalla suddenly thought: the *kubla*! Let the wisest of all midwives be summoned right away, the one who worked as a trusted consultant for the *cadi*.

The *kubla*, the old experienced *kubla*, arrived and the young wife was examined again. The *kubla* smiled:

'Those foreign doctors! Allah smites the Christians with blindness. Let the entire house be calm! Of course there is a child. But he is sleeping. He will come into the world when the time is ripe, sooner or later. Isn't it common knowledge that children sometimes go to sleep in the womb? Some have slept for as long as twenty years and are then called "twenty-year-olds" right at their birth. The honourable *cadi* himself can attest to that. The child doesn't yet make himself felt, but Fadila is no longer menstruating — therefore the child exists. Now patience, only patience, faithful ones!'

When the *kubla* left, several handsome banknotes were crumpled up in the knot of her headcloth, and the meal she ate that day was the tastiest she had eaten for a long time. She had honestly fulfilled her task. Lalla Habiba, the doting mother, once again had her peace of mind.

Another month went by. Lalla Zohra announced a feast — the same Lalla Zohra from whom I had first learned of Fadila's existence. It had been a long time since she had last had a special reason for throwing a party — all her sons had been circumcised, and it would be a long time before they married. Therefore she had her hands and feet decorated with henna. It would be a disgrace for her husband, Sidi Moktar, not to invite female relatives and friends to celebrate such an auspicious event.

I had hardly entered the room when I noticed Lalla Habiba among the other guests. As I held out my hand to her in greeting, everyone eyed us curiously.

It is so pleasant to be a guest in a Moroccan home. The hosts have only one prescription: let the guests relax. Let them spread themselves, lean on the cushions, and listen to the love stories flowing from the record-player rented for the occasion. They must not tire their brains with such a complex and tiresome endeavour as conversation! As we all gave ourselves up silently to the present moment, Lalla Habiba cleared her throat in a bellicose way and turned toward me:

'And how is the *tbib*?'

'Thank you for asking, and may Allah bless you. He will be here himself soon.'

'Is that so?' Then Lalla Habiba announced in a loud triumphant voice: 'Lalla Fadila will soon be giving birth!' She lifted her arms in an arc and intertwined her fingers, forming a broad circle in the air in front of her belly: 'Her belly is like *that*!' Now the whole company had witnessed how Lalla Habiba had scored off the *tbib*!

The *tbib*'s voice could be heard in the patio. The women peered through the gridded window to catch a glimpse of the subject of their discussion. The physician did not come upstairs, but went towards Sidi Moktar's room. After a while I went below to offer greetings to the host. Lalla Habiba followed me.

'Ah, how are you?' the *tbib* asked her good-humouredly. The host had already encircled his seat with tea tray and cakes. 'And how is Lalla Fadila keeping?'

The mother was not in a hurry to answer. Respectfully she kissed Sidi Moktar's shoulder, sat down next to the *tbib*, and crossed her legs under her glittering festive gown. Hands on hips, she finally announced:

'Fadila will soon give birth!'

'Is that so? And may I ask to what she will be giving birth!'

Lalla Habiba's eyes flashed:

'To a child!' She clenched her fists and humped her back. She glared menacingly into the *tbib*'s face:

'I will personally bring you the child to see! Look, with those very hands I will bring him!' she shouted heatedly and shook her fists. The *tbib*'s voice sounded grave as he shot back:

'All right, bring me the child. But you had better make sure you do not bring me another woman's child, because then I'll take action!'

Lalla Habiba's arms went limp, and she looked blank. Then she slowly pulled herself up and left the room.

Had the *tbib*'s words hit the mark? Had the mother begun to doubt her capacity to wait serenely for her daughter to give birth — an event which had been delayed indefinitely? The city had plenty of babies available for a small amount of cash, to speed up the action and ensure Fadila's happiness. As a mother, wasn't it her duty to safeguard her daughter's future? How had that foreign doctor ferreted out her inmost thoughts?

And again weeks passed. No child was born. The circle of Lalla Habiba's acquaintances became ever more excited. They split into two camps: some hinted that the foreign doctor might possibly be right, while others believed the *kubla*. There were even those in whose opinion Fadila had been with child and had given birth in the physician's office — and the childless *tbib* was supposed to have appropriated the baby himself.

However, all the factions agreed on one thing: that this confusion had been caused by the bride stumbling at a Christian on her wedding day. The *djnun*, those sinister beings, had immediately made use of this peculiar incident to blight Ben Ahmed's and Fadila's life together.

FATE INTERVENES

Lalla Fadila squatted at the chafing dish in her father's home and made pancakes out of bread dough. I sat on a carpet corner facing her and watched the cakes expand in the sizzling oil. Fadila removed them from the heat with slow and sure moves, and folded them over several times. At once she pulled the skillet off the fire and asked me:

'Do you sometimes meet Ben Ahmed?'

'Once in a while.'

Why had she asked that question? How did Fadila feel about Ben Ahmed? Had she perhaps fallen in love with him?

'Lalla Fadila, tell me: do you love him?'

She replaced the skillet on the fire and spread the dough on it. Then she looked at me squarely:

'I want Ben Ahmed. I want him badly.'

'But didn't he beat you, as everyone says?'

'He never did.' Fadila raised her head, looked around to make sure she would not be overheard, and said in a low voice: 'When you see Ben Ahmed, tell him that I want him and his house.'

'But . . .' I stuttered, 'are you willing to cohabit with the *chikha*?'

The bottle with oil clattered against the floor:

'I hate Bentshinbou! Tell Ben Ahmed to divorce her! And then I'll go back. That is how I want it.'

I could not convey Fadila's message. Less than a week later, Ben Ahmed had an accident; he drove his car into a telegraph pole. Ben Ahmed was no longer among the living.

Don't cry and be sad, little Fadila! You are still very young. All your life, all your best years, are ahead. As soon as the mourning period of four months and ten days is over, some new suitor will come to bring you happiness, and your life will flow into a proper course.

Allah akbar! God is the greatest of all. Nothing happens to a person unless it has already been inscribed by Him in that person's Book of Fate. Allah alone gives and takes, at His own pleasure.

MOURNING THE COURT COUNCILLOR

(1935)

The air was especially luminous and softly fresh on that morning in early summer. The sky was still a clear blue and had not yet wrapped itself in the warm noonday haze. In the souks the sun shining through the sparse roof of reeds made a pattern on the well-swept ground like a checkered rug. I was on my way to the house of Sherif Abdelaziz. Every patch of sunlight on which I stepped seemed to say: 'The *sherif* is dead!' I would never again meet this sympathetic grey-haired acquaintance of mine. The former court councillor of sultan Moulay Hafid, a major figure of a past era in Morocco and a man of high intelligence with a refined sense of humour, had died the previous day.

Turning the corner at the mosque I slowed my pace. I was in a walled passage somewhat wider than the average for Marrakech, which showed I was near the end of my journey. At a bend further down the street the mosaic basin of a public fountain glittered in the morning radiance. Today the *sherif*'s house door in the wall on my left was wide open. Some figures in burnouses were leaning against the door frame. Ali, the doorguard, rose and came to meet me. His coffee-coloured face had a grey look, and his eyes were red with weeping.

'*Slema*,' he said, in greeting ('May peace be with you'). He pulled me into the dark hallway decorated with daggers and rifles; it was filled with a crowd of men. Sunshine emanated from the patio, where the flowers were as bright as ever. But the high double doors of the surrounding rooms were all shut, except for one room where a white silk cloth hung in the doorway. Behind that curtain Sherif Abdelaziz was presumably lying on a rush mat covering the floor, all hidden in funeral drapes.

Because he had died in the evening, he could not be buried the same day. Thus he had spent his last night above the earth in a completely deserted room, with a candle at his head and a clay pitcher by his side: his soul might still yearn for a drop of water.

He belonged not to men any longer but to Allah, and he was to be taken to the cemetery that very morning.

In a spacious niche at one end of the patio, where till recently the *sherif* had liked to recline and read while listening to the fountain, a group of brethren of the Aissaoua sect, packed close together, were singing in a monotonous drawl. I passed the room where the dead man lay and pulled open the parlour door. Two rows of women facing each other cowered on sitting mattresses, all clothed in white. Only her deep sighs enabled me to distinguish Lalla Fatna, the young widow. The condolence formulae that I had memorised at home seemed superfluous. She wiped her eyes: 'See, he was expected to recover, but now he's dead.' The widow sighed once again, accompanied by a chorus of lament. I stretched out on a mattress.

In this large warm room death did not look so very horrible. The sparse rush mats attached to the outside of the arched white- and yellow-paned windows softened the light. The rhythmic chant from the patio had a soporific effect. The women sat motionless, with *haiks* drawn over their heads or slipping off to the shoulders. The ladies' white fingers clasped handkerchiefs while the dark hands of the black servants clutched the folds of their scarves. They were like Mary Magdalenes frozen in postures of sorrow. Behind the green window mats, roses glowed, begonias flamed, and the almond leaves shone as if varnished. Behind the bushes the brethren of various sects would take turns in their chanting, but the sound was continuous.

Lalla Fatna sat with closed eyes, her white mourning gown massed up around her. Her hair and forehead were carefully wrapped in a white scarf tied at the chin in a knot becoming to a widow; it made her look like a nun. She leaned her cheek against her hand, and all at once snoring sounded through the silent room; the preceding heavy hours of night had taken their toll of her.

According to the messenger who brought me the sad news, the *sherif*'s brother had pronounced the confession of faith loud and clear in the ear of the dying man. He had then waited for the soul to depart, and closed the eyes: a corpse left with the eyes open was believed to invite new deaths in the house. The rooms and the patio had filled with women's crying. Lalla Fatna had at first stood near the body as if petrified, but then, as the reality sank in, she ran out of the room sobbing, threw herself on the ground in the patio pathway, and scratched her face with her fingernails. The *sherif*'s brother had shouted: 'Allah is great! Praise be to Allah!'

The clamour had attracted the women of the neighbourhood. The news spread like wildfire, and soon the house was full to bursting with women, all shouting and wailing. The death chamber was soon cleared of all furniture. The long sitting mattresses were dragged out, and the wall mirrors were covered over with drapes. The floor was washed with large amounts of water, one bucketful after another being thrown down.

The corpse washers had arrived, bringing their wooden frame with holes made in the bottom. As required by custom, the water kettle was put on a fire in the street, next to the house door. After the body had been washed, all its orifices were plugged. Pieces of cotton dipped in rose water were placed on eyes, ears, and mouth.

Meanwhile, five metres of white cotton fabric had been brought from the souks and torn to pieces out of which trousers, shirt, and even slippers were formed for the corpse. A kerchief was wrapped around the head, and a piece of cloth inscribed with a verse from the Koran was placed on the forehead. Then the rest of the *sherif*'s body was wrapped in cloth. Before tying the shroud finely pestled rose petals, incense, and cloves were poured in it.

The gravedigger had come to take the exact measurements. The *tolbas* (praying brethren) had chanted verses from the Koran throughout the whole night. Lalla Fatna's father had stroked her hair: 'Why are you crying? Instead, say "Allah be praised"!'

How many times had I been in this room, conversing happily! Today the mattresses on which the women sat were bare, their velvet covers removed, and the small cushions missing. But the rest of the room was not in a mourning mood. The high ceiling, where countless blooms were painted on a black background, haughtily extended its chandelier. The wall had a broad band of blue mosaic at the height of the matresses, topped by glittering brocade fabric and, still higher, a beautiful collection of paintings and ancient Chinese plates. The fireplace, flanked by carved and gilded glass cases, looked cold and aloof. In a corner an ebony wardrobe, richly covered with nacre intarsia — it had once been the property of King Alfonso XII of Spain — made an impressive sight. Shelves and showcases were full of the vases which the *sherif*, an enthusiastic collector, had picked up on his journeys. Cherished by their owner, they now looked forlorn.

Lalla Fatna was quite a wealthy widow. Being childless, she was entitled only to one-eighth of her husband's inheritance, but on the day before his death the *sherif* had declared in the presence of witnesses: 'The house with everything in it must go to Lalla Fatna.' The aged *sherif* was so very fond of his young wife. But could this uneducated child of nature sitting next to me appreciate all these art treasures? Did Lalla Fatna realise what an extraordinary inheritance had fallen to her? Hardly. No history or geography lessons had piled names and dates into her virginal mind. Like a child fond of pictures, she enjoyed the flowers and birds on the vases, but the dragon on the Chinese plates was bad, nasty, repellent.

The funeral chant outside the room came to a halt. A long single line of burnouses flickered through the window mats as they rose and withdrew. A new line took its place without delay, and the chant started anew, with the vigour of well-rested throats. It kept to a single note. How gloomy it was! Among the women one could only hear: 'Allah . . . Allah . . .'

Lalla Fatna, you who doze here, what will be the form of your future life? The age-old traditions of your country and creed have already determined who will be your future life companion: your dead husband's brother, who will also inherit the major share of the *sherif*'s wealth. Your time of widowhood will pass, those four months and ten days during which, as if entombed yourself, you must not leave these rooms. When you go to the public baths to shed your mourning gown, when you dress up and invite your relatives and friends to the feast — will you not feel the need to laugh and be young again? Won't even your brother-in-law seem an acceptable mate then? Fate has designed for you a gracious path of life, Lalla Fatna.

The widow was awakened by the creaking of the door. A servant girl led in a voluminous figure whose dark eyes in the slit of her face cover searched around. Finding the mistress of the house, the newcomer threw her arms around her, and exclaimed:
'Oh, my daughter!'
Then, with a torrent of lament, she threw herself at Lalla Fatna's feet, but her intense sobbing soon became a forced wail. The other women did not remain idle bystanders: they lamented and wiped their eyes. When the newcomer crouching on the rug finally quietened down, a crumpled old face emerged from her kerchiefs and surprisingly soon took on an air of indifference. The old woman fumbled about on all fours for a few steps, then pulled herself up and quickly took a seat at the low window, her nose pressed against the glass with curiosity.

The howling dirge outside the window, with its single note, tore at the ear-drums and drilled into the brain. At last it made a final loop and stopped. But what wonderful music was bursting out now? A high-pitched male voice started a melodious song, accompanied by the sound of heavy panting in a three-quarters rhythm.

'The *derkaouas*,' the old lady mumbled, as she looked through the window. The word passed through the room, like an echo from mouth to mouth: 'The *derkaouas*!' Was a mystical bird suddenly gliding over our heads in the room, its wings casting a pall over us? The widow shuddered and opened her eyes. Sleepily she smacked her lips, then woke for good. What? Already the *derkaouas* were singing? That meant that her husband, the *sherif*, was leaving his home. Leaving his house and his wife, never to return. Lalla Fatna jerked her head back. A wild hooting moan emerged from her throat.

Something compelled me to make my farewells. I felt it was indecent for me, belonging to an alien creed, to distract the women at this hour in the expression of their emotions. As I left the room, I was confronted by a strange sight: two rows of men faced each other, bending and rising like automatons. This was the source of that ghastly panting, produced by the mechanical compression and dilatation of the lungs.

It was time to glance for a last time towards the white curtain, where people were bustling — the *mokhaznees*, the pasha's gendarmes in their red-tufted caps. Government representatives were also here to take their part in the former court councillor's funeral.

I knew what would follow after my departure. A few more minutes of that strange song, then the body would be placed on the bier. Because he was a *sherif*, a descendant of the Prophet Mohammed, he would be covered by a green velvet cloth. The last journey of Sherif Abdelaziz would begin. As if they were afraid of being late at the cemetery, the pallbearers followed by mourners would proceed at a brisk pace, chanting the credo in time with their steps:

'*La-ilah-illa-Allah, Mo-hammed rasoul Allah!*'

There is no god but Allah, and Mohammed is His prophet. The chant continued uninterruptedly all the way to the cemetery. Carried on the heads of the two bearers, the *sherif* too seemed in a hurry.

Back at home, meanwhile, the wailing Lalla Fatna was wallowing in the dust, accompanied by the women's loud ritual hooting. Once custom had been satisfied, the crying had to stop. The time for lament was over, and those who continued to weep and bawl would be fighting Allah. Allah is the one who gives and takes, so why should the mourners be obstinate?

Furthermore, the domestic tasks awaited. The large round tables were carried out into the patio. The men would soon return from the cemetery, and neighbours and relatives already stood at the door with refreshments for them: hot tea and coffee, and bread with butter and honey.

In the evening the *sherif*'s friends and male relatives would gather to commemorate him at a funeral supper, including couscous. Some twenty *tolbas* would be present to chant and pray. The dishes were prepared at the relatives' homes, since for two days no fire could be lit in the *sherif*'s house. There could be no laundering for seven days.

In the early morning of the third day women would go to the grave, the widow excepted. They would take along bread and dried figs to distribute to the poor at the cemetery. On their way back they would buy meat and vegetables to prepare *tajines*, and then it would be their turn to commemorate the deceased.

Our friend Sherif Abdelaziz was resting in the dry soil of Marrakech. No flowers decorated his grave. In Marrakech they say: flowers will wilt. The dead cannot see or smell them. The dead belong to Allah and His laws. All earthbound concerns have fallen away like a dirty cloth. Why take such garbage as flowers to the grave? The Arabs smile, sympathetically and rather disapprovingly, when they see Europeans taking fresh flowers to the graves of their loved ones in the European quarter of the city.

ELIMINATION FROM THE HAREM

(1930)

The term 'harem' designates the living space which a Muslim man allocates to his wife or wives, be it in a palace, a hut or a tent in the desert. In the West its meaning has shifted from the living space to the women enclosed within it, preferably numerous and in splendid surroundings. The harem! What connotations of oriental glamour! Dozens of charming and desirable young women, with or without veils, resting on silken pillows by fountains in marble palaces.

Early Western travellers were adept, in their writings, at making the harem appear resplendent and magnificent. Being out of bounds for them behind locked doors, it bred fantasy. Some of them tried to delve into the inner lives of harem women, even to the point of commiserating with them—like the French writer Pierre Loti, mystified by a compatriot who passed herself off as a Turkish lady and provoked him with her letters.

'Harem' actually derives from the adjective 'haram' or 'hram' which means 'shameful' or even 'sinful'. In everyday language it simply means 'forbidden'. A good Muslim divides his home into two parts: the haram-like and the salam-like. A non-related male entering the house must meticulously avoid the haram-like part. Keep out: this is where the other man's wives are! He has to direct his steps towards the salam-like section where he will be a welcome guest.

'Salam!' is the usual greeting exchanged when two Muslims meet. It bids heavenly bliss after death. A Muslim always greets another in a dignified plural: never just 'Salam alik!' (May bliss be with thee), but 'Salam alikum!' (May bliss be with you). This is because the greeting addresses not only the person encountered but also his two invisible guardian angels who walk on his left and right. 'Salam' does not apply to Christians and Jews, to whom the Muslim bids only 'slema' — welfare on this earth.

Around 1880, when Sultan Moulay Hassan ruled Morocco, a

self-respecting man of substance would have four legal wives, a bevy of concubines, female slaves beyond counting, and up to fifty children. A hundred years later, with the sultan's namesake King Moulay Hassan II on the throne, the bell could be tolled for the harem. A new age has asserted itself triumphantly. Moroccan youth is monogamous, and the practice of keeping two wives lives on only among the wealthy of the older generation. Houses have become small, or one may even live in an apartment. Finding servants has become a headache for the matrons, because girls are obliged to go to school. The ancient white *haik* has long since been replaced in the streets by the dark *djellaba*, the coat with sleeves that used to be the men's clothing. The beautiful embroidered slippers have given way to shoes. And then suddenly women have ultra-modern costumes, and some — if viewed from the traditional standpoint — even go semi-naked.

The gradual fading away of the harems took place during my long stay in Marrakech. When I arrived, large ones were kept by the magnates and especially the rulers of country districts. I succeeded in casting only a fleeting glimpse into them, but what my eyes and ears managed to apprehend during those brief moments was a far cry from my exaggerated image of harems. There was no poetic or romantic glow about them. Under a bluer sky and in more exuberant clothes than in northern Europe, I found women who were the same as elsewhere, with their daily worries and joys. They were friendly and modest, but very reticent with a foreigner, as good manners required. A Spanish lady who was personally acquainted with the harems of olden times defined them as a bunch of wives, children, servants and slaves who bickered, engaged in backbiting and fought with each other — that was a harem for you!

An old *caid*'s castle on the outskirts of Marrakech comes to my mind. Built of non-fired bricks, this fortress-like manor sheltered the women's house behind it. The single-storeyed harem was long and narrow, with two rows of women's quarters opening on to a common hallway. There were twenty women, or maybe more, and within the walls of their garden they could build a network either of friendship or of envy. The two dominant wives lived in the manor. The older one was quiet and level-headed; the younger (who was also approaching middle age) had thrillingly wide eyes. There was a third woman in the manor, living in a rug-lined room under the stairways, like a solitary canary in a cage. She was the master's current favourite, extremely young, and cheerless to the point of tears.

The last pasha of Marrakech, the legendary great *caid* el-Glaoui, was reputed to have had three hundred wives in the course of his life. This is probably an exaggeration — we could settle for half that number — but if one considers the wide reach of his domain and how many city and mountain castles he owned, counts the religious feasts at which the prettiest maidens from far and near were brought to him as gifts, and does not forget his many aged and pensioned-off wives, it is clear that the total could indeed have approached a couple of hundred.

The door of the harem in the pasha's palace in Marrakech was padlocked, and although I entered some parts of the palace, I never got into this part. Madame Rose, the wife of the pasha's French chauffeur, was the only female allowed to come and go as the needs of the harem ladies required. I knew her, but her mouth also seemed to have a padlock. The most I could find out was that she sometimes bought perfumes for the ladies.

In contrast, I had open access to the home of the pasha's perennial companion, Hadj Kadur. In the scope of their respective powers, those two men could not even be compared. The pasha was like the king of the Berbers, second only to the King of Morocco himself; Kadur was merely one of the pasha's officials. Whereas the pasha possessed up to three hundred wives, Hadj Kadur — even though he was a respected citizen and was well off — had to make do with only three. He did not even take concubines.

The pretty and charming Lalla Zaleha was Hadj Kadur's first wife. When after several years of marriage she did not become pregnant and Hadj Kadur hinted ever more frequently at her being barren, Lalla Zaleha undertook an act of anguished self-abnegation: she herself pushed her young servant Keltoum into her husband's arms. The plump clear-faced Keltoum was modest and obedient by nature — there was no risk of her outgrowing her mistress's control. Life seemed to have reached calmer waters. However, Allah did not deign to bless Lalla Keltoum's womb either.

When a new additional wife stepped into the house, both existing wives were thunderstruck. Who was this tall woman with enticing contours? None other than Lalla Hafida, well known to the men of the city. She was a musician who used to play under the direction of the Egyptian conductor of the pasha's orchestra. Opinions differed regarding this marriage. Most of those in the know maintained that it was the pasha who had bestowed her on his faithful official as a gift. Others said that Hadj Kadur himself had asked the pasha for her.

Immediately, the bold and energetic Lalla Hafida asserted herself in Hadj Kadur's household. Unflinchingly and with a despotic will, she assailed the existing ways and roles of the household members. She quickly subdued Lalla Keltoum, who had never had much say anyway, but she also asserted her will and demands in the face of mild-natured Lalla Zaleha. By seizing the pantry and storage room keys, she made her control complete. Lalla Zaleha looked resigned, but deep inside she nursed a dark hatred for the second co-wife. Lalla Hafida had come to the house with the hope of outdoing the existing wives by presenting Hadj Kadur with a string of sons, but she had to reach the dismaying conclusion that it was precisely this mild and innocuous-looking Zaleha who must have thwarted her hopes and plans. How so? By witchcraft, undoubtedly! Hafida's rage against Zaleha grew.

Several years went by. Hafida put on weight, yet she kept her figure: the fat covered her statuesque body evenly. A goodly double chin indicated a life without worry, but also without movement. As for Lalla Zaleha, her health was not as good as it might have been, while Lalla Keltoum's beauty reached its peak. Then came the fasting period during which one of them was eliminated.

THE MONTH OF SHA'BAN

It was the year 1348 in the Islamic calendar, and its most important month was approaching: Ramadan, the month of fasting during which all daytime eating and drinking stops. This period of spiritual and physical cleansing started to be mentioned several months beforehand. When the immediately preceding month of Sha'ban arrived, the general mood was one of excitement. Some older people trained for the great fast by not eating for a couple of days. Trade was brisk. People were selling, buying and completing any necessary trips to the countryside or to other cities. The young celebrated weddings. One should eat, drink and enjoy life before the period of humility began!

By an unusual chance Hadj Kadur's massive cedarwood door with carvings and decorative studs was open one late afternoon in Sha'ban. A servant girl's head even protruded from the door slit. As she saw me, she called '*Slema!*' and then announced my arrival by shouting, into the hallway: '*Mada-ame!*'

The girl's relaxed behaviour told me that the master of the house was out and the women were alone. This was further confirmed by the presence of the doorguard Shiban, a bearded and toothless old man, cowering on the ground and leaning against the house wall next to the door. He guarded Hadj Kadur's door day and night, like a faithful watchdog. To make his task easier, he had been lodged on the opposite side of the narrow alley, sharing a modest shelter with the master's three cows and a couple of sheep. His crumpled figure could almost always be seen hanging about the street, except when he was running errands for the household or when the master was at home; on those occasions the door was bolted from the inside, and Shiban was freed for the time being from his guard duty. As a man of high position, the master was frequently away from home for days and even weeks, and at these times the house guard took on special responsibilities. He was entrusted with the house key, which he carried on a string round his neck under his long gown. It was so important that any criminal hand intending to seize it would have to kill him first.

Since the master had graciously authorised visits to his wives by certain female acquaintances, there was no reason for Shiban to be stern and strict. Under his rough surface he hid a soft heart which at times made him take boyish risks: he would actually push the door half open, thus allowing servants and even the ladies to look out into the street. On this occasion too I witnessed Shiban's indulgences. I stepped over the high threshold into the hall, where a row of brass water containers stood in holes cut into a wooden bench, and followed the bends in the hallway to the central patio.

Hadj Kadur's house was not particularly large. Essentially, the ground floor contained only the three wives' chambers. As one entered the tile-covered patio, Lalla Hafida's bedroom was behind the white pillars on the left. The door on the right led to Lalla Zaleha's room, while the room directly facing the hallway was occupied by the youngest wife, Lalla Keltoum. Each of these chambers had two low but wide arched windows flanking the tall double door which was usually kept open. This floor also included the pantry, a servants' room, and a narrow opening in the patio wall. This bottleneck led to the nearly lightless kitchen where some pots perennially simmered over charcoal, with a few primitive shelves above. Two old black women squatted near the pots. Like moles they spent their lives in that cave, soiled with coal dust and soot, their faces greyish brown, and their watery eyes shunning light.

The whole ground floor belonged to the women and thus represented the *haram*-like part of the house. The men's *salam*-like part was on the upper floor — it could be reached directly from the hallway via a high-stepped stone stairway.

The male reception room was above Lalla Hafida's chamber, and it had thoughtfully been supplied with a balcony which blocked the view to the patio. Next to it was the master's private bedroom, which contained a genuine European bed always in a perfect state of readiness. I doubt if he ever found time to use it, except when he was ill, since he had to divide his nights among his several spouses. A small room next-door even had an outmoded bathtub, but this was an object of pride rather than convenience, since the water for it had to be carried up in pails. The whole household usually went to the city baths on a specially reserved night.

All the rooms on both floors were necessarily narrow, since the split palm beams that supported the ceilings could not bear much weight, but, as if by way of compensation, they were long and high. The furnishings were the usual: carpets stretching from wall to wall, and wool-packed sitting mattresses lining the walls. In contrast to the airy rooms with their precious carpets, the patio offered little to the eye. Too small for trees to be planted, it was covered with stone slabs, except for a central opening to carry away rain and floor washing water.

As I reached the patio on that particular day I was greeted by a rather motley scene. All the women had abandoned the rooms and settled themselves on rugs spread among the pillars in the patio, in the shadow of the balcony. The February sun was already too hot. What a gypsy camp — with women, bare-bottomed children, tea glasses, servants, slippers, and pillows. Of course, one had to be as merry as possible in the month of Sha'ban. They all seemed in an unusually high good humour. The stoutest of the wives, Lalla Hafida, sat on a pile of pillows, a head taller than anyone else. She wore a violet velvet caftan.

'*Marbabbik!*' Lalla Hafida shouted the welcoming phrase to me in her deep voice, drawing the word aristocratically through the nose. She added imperiously:

'Come and sit next to me.' I made my way to her, and we shook hands.

'*Labes?*' she asked, using a politeness formula equivalent to 'How are you?' but literally meaning 'not bad'.

'*Labes,*' I answered.

'*El hamdulillah!* Praised be Allah. Is the *tbib labes?*'

'*Labes,* thank you.'

'Is your home *labes?*'

'*Labes.*'

'Is your health *labes?*'

'*Labes.*'

'Are your next-of-kin *labes?*'

'*Labes.*'

I had barely completed this volleyball match of '*labes*' when the other wives tackled me with the same questions. The slim Lalla Zaleha posed her series of '*labes*' in a teasing way, as she somewhat lazily propped herself up from her comfortable reclining position.

Her mop of tresses had slipped from the top of her head down her back. The youngest spouse was expected to be alert, so Lalla Keltoum stood up from behind the tray where she had been sitting cross-legged, preparing tea. She was small and smiled agreeably like a nice Estonian farm girl.

The servants came and kissed me on the shoulder. The pock-marked Aunt Yamina's head was, as always, wrapped in a yellow cotton kerchief as if she had a permanent tooth-ache. She reproached me for not having visited them for so long. Lalla Ftuh echoed her, making wide hand gestures. An uglier sight than Lalla Ftuh's face was hard to find: a bout of syphilis had ravaged it horribly, completely destroying her nose and leaving only a hole so that her speech came out as an almost unintelligible snuffle. Despite the handicap of her looks, Lalla Ftuh was wise and pleasant-natured, and those who came to know her rediscovered the old truth that true human value is independent from the outer shell.

Aunt Yamina was a permanent guest in Hadj Kadur's house, and she always spent the night in the chamber of one or another of the wives. In contrast, Lalla Ftuh came only occasionally to visit her five-year-old son Rbib, a ward of the master of the house and the ingratiatingly elfin favourite of his three wives. Prodded by his mother, Rbib cautiously approached me to kiss my hand. But mistrust, inspired by my European clothes, made him suddenly stop half-way. He pursed his lips, blew a kiss in my direction, and ran post-haste back to his mother's lap. Moments later he was again fooling around with the head servant Hashouma's urchin, Bubkir. They had a pillow fight and rolled on the ground.

Keltoum's mother and Rahel the Jewess had come to take part in the feasting before Ramadan, during which one could spend the whole day eating and drinking to one's heart's content. They were welcome in the harem. The tea kettle was on the charcoals almost the whole time anyway, and the house was not short of couches for sitting or reclining. Let the guest relax, sip tea and tell the latest news. In conformity with this practice, Hashouma immediately placed a hot tea glass in my hand and built up a back support of wool pillows against a pillar. Having the harem walls around me and the patch of blue sky above my head, there was nothing to prevent me from partaking of the life of Moorish women and even from fantasising that I myself was one of them hidden behind locked doors.

Rahel seemed to be the heroine of the day. She was middle-aged and had a muddy complexion and short, swollen legs. I was familiar with her somewhat naive goodwill and the humbly submissive look of her brown eyes. Rahel moved around in Hadj Kadur's house as if she belonged there. In spite of coming from the despised Jewish stock, she had become a friend of the ladies of the house. Indeed she was indispensable to them. No Arab of any wealth could live without the services of the Jews. After the battles of ancient times, Jews were given the task of salting the enemies' heads before they were exhibited on city walls. 'Melh' is salt, and the mellah is the Jewish quarter of the city. The Jewish readiness to oblige has survived to this day. They will lend money, or they will offer themselves as go-betweens in complex negotiations. Who else but the Jewess could perform the tasks outside the harem walls needed by Hadj Kadur's women? Rahel's main occupation was to use her rickety old sewing machine to run up pairs of underpants for the local French garrison, but her harem connections were cosy and lucrative: no one there objected to her sitting around for the entire day if she felt like it, eating good rich food and spending the night.

Today Rahel had brought along a great pile of samples of materials. She had gone through the entire mellah and the souks, tearing a strip from one roll of cloth, cutting a sliver from another, begging each merchant for a price reduction and a commission for herself. Now Lalla Hafida fingered these slivers. She inspected them one by one with the utmost calm and unflinching self-confidence, knowing exactly what she was after. No, she didn't like that red. This thin stuff with black-spotted stripes and yellow yarn — that was an improvement. But nothing can beat white silk — here her search came to an end, and she would take five metres instead of the usual three and a half. After all, she was not thin, thank God, but tall, with a reasonable amount of fat on her bones. Let Rahel get her this cloth from the store the very next morning. During the fast a self-respecting married woman must be in white.

Aunt Yamina joined the servants in loudly approving of Lalla

Hafida's choice. They had long since fallen into the habit of automatically supporting anything she said or did. But Lalla Zaleha and Lalla Keltoum acted in a strangely passive way towards Hafida's doings and towards the cloth samples. Both held themselves aloof from the attractions of the slivers. Zaleha continued resting on her back, and Keltoum sat at her tea tray with an air of indifference. Why this lack of interest on the part of the co-wives? Was it not their main task, too, to dress up for their husband and thus be forever buying new clothes? The reason was elementary: why be tempted by something which you could not afford? They all had the same husband, but their purses were unequal.

It was not that Hadj Kadur would sin against the Koran by favouring one of his wives and neglecting the others. No, he was too loyal and kind-hearted a husband for that, and too devout a believing Muslim. On this he could not be reproached either by others or by his own conscience. He followed the holy prescriptions to the letter, feeding his wives well, supplying them with clothes that were equal in price and quality, and dispensing his husbandly tenderness to them in a rotation of nights. To have done otherwise would have invited immediate retribution for his sins, in the form of a poisoned home atmosphere. Rather than have to cope with that, it would be preferable to act like a poor man, keeping only one wife at a time and exchanging her for a new one, as one's wishes and opportunities might dictate.

As for Lalla Hafida, she was able to make her purchases from her personal funds, which seemed pretty plentiful — all the francs which had rolled in during her career as a performing artist. It was also said that she possessed valuable jewellery which she did not wear but kept hidden in the wool of her couch.

I watched Lalla Hafida as she rummaged through the samples. Her features were regular, the skin an onion yellow; she had rather small dark brown eyes, a well-formed mouth, and a small, slightly hooked nose. Her nostrils never ceased quivering, and her whole personality expressed energy, self-assurance and a will to dominate. Her clothes emphasised those qualities. She always wore heavy-falling cloth, bold colours and the accessories about her person were adorned with metal, like the gold-embroidered belt which today compressed her imposing waist. The two multi-coloured kerchiefs tied turbanlike round her head made her seem more like a priestess than an ordinary woman.

What a contrast, both in character and looks, between her and Lalla Zaleha! The first wife had certainly not lost her wit and humour. There she lay on her back, slender and delicate, her eyes wide open and staring skywards. Her lithe-fingered hands, one of which she now held behind her neck, were exceedingly beautiful, as were her slightly arched feet that protruded from under her light grey gown. The term 'princess' came spontaneously to mind, but the princess's facial expression did not betoken happiness. Something like fatigue, but reverie too, flitted across her high forehead and perfectly clear-skinned milk-white face on which, at moments, her eyelashes cast shadows. But the corners of the mouth betrayed bitterness, and the lips were pursed. Everything about Lalla Zaleha suggested a rare house-plant which has been deprived of sunshine.

A gem-studded golden butterfly adorned Lalla Zaleha's breast, and her least movement gave a tremble to the *louis d'or* that hung from her ears. The other ladies were also decked out in their finery. As the fast approached, one should carry all one's wealth and enjoy it. Soon Ramadan would arrive, the grey month in which all jewellery, lipstick and other make-up are banned. Lalla Keltoum had attached a large golden brooch to her kerchief, but Lalla Hafida wore about her neck a bizarre wide ornament that defied description. My curiosity was whetted.

'Lalla Hafida, what are you wearing round your neck?'

Without a word Lalla Hafida unplucked the ornament and threw it in my lap. It was a thick and heavy pleat of pearls. A green stone joined two skeins, each with twelve strings of pearls, making a total of twenty-four necklaces. Lopsided lentil-sized beads were strung on them: genuine pearls. A fortune hung there!

'That must have cost quite a lot?' I ventured. Hafida nodded appraisingly:

'Quite a lot indeed.'

I glanced at Zaleha: she must be envious. The princess's mouth had pulled itself into a contemptuous smirk. Hafida too watched

Zaleha out of the corner of her eye and seemed to want to snap out something at her, but restrained herself, tightened her lips, and gestured to a servant to refasten the necklace round her neck. Lalla Hafida's irritation amused Zaleha and instantly lightened her mood. She got busy teasing the children. Rbib threw pillows at her, skipped about, rolled over and laughed. The tiny Bubkir's frock had been rolled up and tightened at his chest so that it would not be dirtied if there were a mishap. With his stomach and bottom bare, the child shrieked with laughter, and stumbled and fell all the time in the lap of Zaleha, who kissed him and tossed him on to other women.

No one wanted any more tea; all seemed to have been saturated with this sweet yellow syrup which only made one thirsty again. The servant girls Zohra and Ms'ouda were kept busy passing a clay container of cold water, sometimes to Aunt Yamina and sometimes to Lalla Ftuh, as it was called for. At a gesture by Lalla Keltoum, Zohra collected the glasses and the tray with teapots, took them to the furthest corner of the patio, and washed them. The ladies yawned, stretched, shifted around, chattered. 'How many days until the fast begins?' I asked Lalla Zaleha.

'Three or four. It would depend on the new moon, and when it first appears.' She turned her whole body round to face me and pouted comically:

'Yes, a few more days and that is the end of the good month of Sha'ban. Good-bye to the good times!' She threw her arms over her head and stretched out to her full length:

'Allah-ah! One can't eat or drink in the day, or even sniff perfumes. Every year I lose five or six kilos of my health during the fast. By the end of it I will look like that . . .' She sucked in her cheeks, rolled her eyes so that only the whites showed, pulled out her chin with both hands — and then burst into a clear laugh, showing her shining teeth.

Hafida frowned again and taxed Zaleha disapprovingly. The look on her face showed how little she appreciated her co-wife. How did Zaleha dare to criticise Allah's commands and complain about them? How could she still expect remission of her sins through fasting? No wonder Allah had barred her from having

children. Hafida gave a disdainful shrug of her shoulders.
Through her half-closed eyelids, Zaleha stole a glance at her
co-wife's darkened brow, and mischievously she picked me as a
relay to launch an arrow at Hafida, saying in French:

'*Lalla Hafida mange beaucoup! Elle est trop grosse!*' — Lalla
Hafida eats a lot, she's too fat.

Hafida strained her ears. Whenever that person brought out her
French vocabulary, Hafida's irritation immediately flared, because
she could not understand what was being said about her. Exhaling
loudly just once, as she always did when she was angry, Hafida
rose brusquely, jutted her jaw, gestured Rahel to join her, and
sailed up the stairs, her head high. The Jewess trotted obediently
after her. Zaleha seemed satisfied with the result of her teasing.
With a fleeting smile, she beckoned me to come closer and whispered:

'When Lalla Hafida gets mad, she always plays sick a bit later.
You'll see! It's her tactic for getting attention.' Then the corners
of her mouth dropped, and she sighed:

'I have to be thick-skinned because the words she throws at
me — these keep nagging at my heart.'

Lalla Zaleha got up:

'It's getting late. I love watching the sunset from the roof.
Then the sun is so big and red.' She put her arm on my shoulder:

'You know, when I was still a girl and lived in Tanja [Tangier],
I went every evening from my roof to that of my neighbour, Lalla
Nezhma. Other young girls from other roofs came too. Lalla
Nezhma could read. She read us poems by Ibn Sahl — he was a
renowned Andalusian bard. And then we took turns composing
poems of our own, simply as the lines flowed from one's brain.
They all applauded mine. We ate roasted melon seeds. Sometimes
Madame Marianne joined us — she spoke French and taught us a
few words. The poems often made me cry. Listen:

> *When the heart has become ashes in the ground,*
> *then you will call me, but it will be too late.*
> *Weeping, you will say: Where is she whom I love?*

Isn't that a beautiful song?'

Before I could respond, Rahel shouted from the balcony that Lalla Hafida was asking me to come upstairs. I found them in the gentlemen's salon, where the high plush-covered mattresses did not bear the impress of people having recently sat on them. Women did not usually come here. The Jewess was busy first spreading out a red-speckled piece of calico on the carpet, and then covering it over with a white sheet. She brought a water pitcher and set it on the floor. Hafida produced a brand-new iron, and the work began. Kneeling on the floor, the Jewess, taking her time, ironed the master's cotton bags. Hafida knelt too and watched Rahel's work intently to ensure that the iron did not scorch the carpet. A bystander would have had the impression that Hafida was a teacher instructing Rahel in the art.

Twilight spread rapidly in the room, and the whoops from the roof reminded me of my promise to go there. From the edge of the roof Lalla Zaleha and little Rbib gestured in my direction. I joined them by climbing up the clumsy high-stepped stairs and as I set my foot on the smooth whitewashed roof, a new world opened before me, and my soul seemed to expand. Around us one could see hundreds of flat roofs, some slightly lower and some higher than ours. The setting sun cast a reddish glimmer on the whitewash and glowed on our faces and hair. Far to the south the snowy crest of the High Atlas was coloured pink. The light of the sky was marvellously clear, and palm trees away at the edge of the city were like tiny cut-outs. Below us, the patio looked like a well bottom teeming with evening shadows. The sound of conversation drifted up — Bubkir still bustled about, and the grey figures of Hafida and Rahel crouched on the upper floor. Here on the roof we had space and light. I seized my camera and took a snapshot of Lalla Zaleha, and when we went down again, I snapped Lalla Hafida as well.

It was now high time for me to return home — I had not told anybody of my intention to visit the harem. I made my farewells and knocked on the outer door to give Shiban a signal. There was no response.

'Hey, Shiban, open up!'

There seemed to be no sign of Shiban. The door in all its

massiveness remained shut and was not to be shaken by the wom-
en's fist-banging and shouting. It was padlocked from the outside. I was a prisoner.

My previous fantasy of being one of the harem ladies had
become an unpleasant reality. Lalla Ftuh cheered me up:

'He must have gone to the souks to buy food. He will not be
long.'

In Lalla Zaleha's opinion the old man had gone to the mosque
for the evening prayers. Lalla Hafida thought I was getting upset
about nothing.

'Come,' she said. 'We can sit in my room.'

Rahel was already there. The loss of freedom gave her no
concern. She was used to spending some nights in the harem.
Electric lights came on in the patio and the chambers. The customary greetings were exchanged: *Msakum!* Good evening! And one
would decorously respond right and left: *Msalhir!* — Blessings
come in the evening. Servants and children rushed to kiss the
matrons' hands.

The whole household gathered in Lalla Hafida's room. It was
getting cool outside, but in here it was comfortable and warm.
Before Lalla Hafida's arrival in the house, this room had served as
the living-room, and by force of old habit meals were still taken
here. During meal-times a low round table was rolled in and
placed in front of the sitting mattresses at one end of the room, filling up the corner. At the other end were Lalla Hafida's wide
woollen couch and the clothes chest behind it.

How lavishly Hafida had decorated this place! The canopy
above her mattress was of shiny silk-satin draped with green atlas.
An appliqué carpet covered the longer wall. The door and
the arched windows were topped with white satin hemmed with
pink lace and ruffled rosettes of a sky-blue colour. The floor rug
was not the ordinary handmade kind but much fancier: it was
machine-produced. The gilt-framed mirror on the wall stood out
less by its silk and spangle trimming than by the photos of Sultan
Mohammed V surrounding it — twenty of them.

Our conversation got bogged down. What can you talk about
with harem denizens, anyway? Their experiences outside the

house walls? That was impossible. Gossip? There was an amazing amount of that, but it was better left for confidential whispering. Events inside the house? This topic was disallowed by the custom of extreme reserve and reticence. Children? Yes, that would have been a fertile topic, but this house had no children of its own. The sleepy Rbib had curled up behind Lalla Ftuh's back, and the tiny Bubkir was probably asleep in the servants' room.

The matrons sat idle, tightly side by side. They lacked this peculiarly European need to be isolated from one's neighbour through an air layer so that flanks would not touch and one's elbow would not push into another's ribs. In this country people were kept together by the feeling of closeness and bodily warmth which produced a sense of belonging and protection. Only Zaleha and Hafida tended to avoid each other's contact. Lalla Zaleha would slip some joking asides into Lalla Hafida's purposely loud talk. As usual, Keltoum talked the least, and even then only in whispers.

Lalla Zaleha's hand slid on the radio set at the window sill. Arab music from Egypt was made available to the people in the late evening when the daytime music meant for the French had ended. Zaleha cautiously turned the knob to get Rabat, the capital of Morocco. With her ear close to the set and a smirk on her face, she listened to the quaint music of the Europeans. The next instant, Lalla Hafida's hand was in the way, and the contest for the knob filled the room with deafening atmospheric whistles and screeching. Then, as usual, Lalla Hafida had her way. The tension that had seized hold of all of us was relieved by the Arab song on the radio.

Time kept flowing past, but Shiban did not return. It was with uneasy feelings that I shared the copious meal. After supper Lalla Hafida ordered the black kitchen woman to massage her stomach, saying she felt unwell. Zaleha gave me a wink — a reminder of her previous remark about her co-wife's sickness gambit. Hafida's belly was wide and monumental like the rest of her. Framed by her white underclothes it resembled a dish full of dough — as it was kneaded by the old woman's palms the soft mass heaved and quivered. Fingers sank into the thick layer of fat. As a final touch

Rahel helped the old woman turn a towel into a rope; and, joining forces, they bound the lower abdomen as tightly as they could, forcing the fat upwards.

Aunt Yamina too complained of a health problem, recurring headaches — but the reaction of many of those present was a burst of laughter. They were well aware of Aunt Yamina's weakness for *kif*, the Moroccan hemp. When she was able furtively to swallow a teaspoonful of *kif* powder mixed in sugar grains her joy became total. She succumbed to blissful dreams and mumbled funny answers to anyone who disturbed her, which made them laugh. Otherwise she was kind, accepting and willing to help anyone. Her senior woman's duties included escorting the harem wives on their nocturnal trips to the public baths. I promised Aunt Yamina to bring her medication against headaches.

It was midnight before Shiban returned and let me out. Although my home was not far from Hadj Kadur's house I was not allowed to go alone but had to follow obediently behind Shiban. He tacked ahead of me in his heelless slippers, and in complete defiance of the electric street lights, he carried a candlestick in one hand, and protected the flame with the other. Only when we reached my house door could I take off like a bird released from its cage and soar into my habitual European life.

THE FAST BEGINS

Ramadan, the month of fasting, would begin any day now, depending on the new moon. All of Marrakech excitedly scanned the evening sky. Streets and squares filled with people. Would a thin edge of the sickle moon appear? Would the fast begin tomorrow, or be delayed for one more day? There they stood, looking up until their necks were stiff. Otherwise the sky was crystal-clear, but a cluster of clouds lay near the horizon. Did those clouds hide the moon? People at last went to their homes undecided, but no one felt like going to sleep.

It was near midnight when with one accord the city people were startled out of their silence and jumped to their feet: trumpets jangling in the streets announced that Ramadan had begun. The pasha had received a telephone call from the capital city. The new moon had been seen in northern Morocco. Everyone — young and old, rich and poor, man and woman — vowed to submit humbly and obediently to the Koran's command to fast during daytime for the whole month.

On the second day of fasting I went to Hadj Kadur's house door to deliver Aunt Yamina's headache medicine. Once again I found the door open — and Lalla Hafida angrily scolding a water-carrier she had cornered in the vestibule.

'Why didn't you bring us any water yesterday?'

The member of the water suppliers' guild, half-naked like a being from the nether world, leaned indifferently against the wall. His brown shanks and thighs were thin like sticks, and a hairy goatskin water bag hung from his shoulder empty. He seemed deaf to all the reproaches met at this house and all the other houses.

'I was sleeping yesterday. The first day of Ramadan . . . I was too weak to . . . Do you need another bagful?'

'Has *Shitan* got into you? Away with you, and come back with more water at once!'

The water-carrier turned about phlegmatically. With his cane he tapped one of the clay vessels lining the wall, and the hollow sound confirmed the absence of water. He sauntered off, knowing that no back-chat was allowed in that house. The ruling matron required submission, and who would dare to challenge her?

On the third evening of Ramadan the *tbib* and I went to pay the customary goodwill visit to Hadj Kadur. The pressures of the *tbib*'s job made us come too late in one sense and too early in another. The *moudens* in the mosque towers had called for prayers at dusk a whole hour earlier, and the hoot of municipal sirens had announced the end of the daytime fast. People had already gulped down their first hurried bowl of post-fast soup. Etiquette demanded that we should have done that in our friend's company, but we had not managed it. On the other hand, it was too early for the main supper. By now the evening prayers were at hand, and most men were off to the mosques where peace and quiet reigned and the communion of prayer elevated the soul. Would we find Hadj Kadur at home?

Shiban cowered at the door in his usual way. His strength had been sapped by three days of Ramadan, or rather by those three cool nights of constant coming and going. He tendered us his rough hand, burst into a cough, hid his nose in his burnous, and pointed to his rattling thorax.

The patio was dark and deserted. The double door into Lalla Zaleha's room was pulled shut. A sliver of light seeped out from underneath. Lalla Keltoum's door was also closed, but Lalla Hafida's was wide open behind the pillars. Her room was brightly lit, and only the flimsy door curtain separated us from the master of the house who knelt praying on the rug under the candelabra. He passed the wooden beads of his rosary through his fingers, each bead representing one of Allah's holy attributes. He rose, and his tall, slender figure filled the whole door opening. He stood upright, his head thrown back and his lips moving. Then kneeling once more, he bowed nimbly, and his forehead touched the floor three times in praise of Allah. For a brief spell he stayed bent over, given up to devotion and submissiveness. The prayer phase called the *rakas* came next. Still kneeling, he supported his body on the balls of his feet, and I knew the words he was now enunciating:

> *Oh Allah, forgive,*
> *Have mercy on me,*
> *Guide me,*
> *Keep me,*
> *Make me better,*
> *Strengthen my faith and enrich me.*

Once again his forehead touched the floor in prayer: Allah is great! Then he remained sitting quietly, fingering his wooden beads on the silken cord. He was aware of our arrival. Still kneeling, he lifted the curtain and silently gave us the sign to enter and be seated. Some beads were still left when he jumped up with an easy movement, hung the rosary over the mirror frame, and shook our hands warmly:

'Be welcome. It is nice of you to come and greet us!'

Hadj Kadur was a man in his prime, with a wiry body in fine condition. His swarthy face was full and his nose straight. His beard descended like a velvet band along his jaw, narrowing to a slender line and forming an upward-pointing triangle at the bottom of his chin. The areas above and below the lips, as well as under the chin, were meticulously shaven. The glance of his dark and slightly oily eyes was sharp, and the high curved forehead seemed able to hide his thoughts. His favourite colours were brown and light blue. Today his loosely falling broadcloth *djellaba* was dark brown. When he sat facing the *tbib* he pulled his feet inside the train of his gown.

The talk soon turned from the customary polite expressions to the fast and the weather. What an unusual cold spell for the fasting month! During the night the thermometer had even dropped below zero centigrade — a truly amazing phenomenon. There had been a shower of hail, which bounced off the palm trees and frayed the leaves of the orange trees. But of course fasting was easier in winter than in the summer heat. The season of Ramadan shifted over the years, since the calendar year was a good ten days shorter than the sun cycle. Every year Ramadan came earlier in the season, and the more it shifted from autumn toward the long days of late summer the harder the fast became, until it reached the season in which the sun burned with its full heat and parched the tongue deprived of the least drop of water. This year, however, Ramadan coincided with the Christians' February. While the cold breath of the High Atlas chilled the nights, the days were comfortable for fasting.

Our host interrupted the conversation to clap his hands. Someone must have been spying behind the door curtain, because the head servant Hashouma entered instantly, carrying a low circular dinner table pressed against her abdomen. Hadj Kadur commented with a smile:

'Of course, I ate a small bowl of *hrira*, the fasting soup, as soon as the sun had set. But one cannot eat more than this right away. The fast makes the stomach shrink like a dry sponge. You swallow just a little thin soup and feel perspiration on your forehead. But now we can eat more. How can one fast throughout the day without eating hearty meals during the night?'

His hand signalled us to approach the table, when Lalla Hafida entered. Clothed all in white and without make-up, she looked pale and even her cheeks seemed hollow. She first walked up to the Hadj and kissed him lightly on the shoulder. Only then did she greet us. At her husband's command she obediently joined us, sitting cross-legged at the table. How this proud Lalla Hafida was changed in Hadj Kadur's presence! She lowered her glance and spoke only a couple of words. Was it really from Lalla Hafida's wide thorax that this small voice emerged? Her nostrils still quivered, but not from any feeling of superiority and self-assertion this time but from sheer humility. Oh, what a clever and wise woman . . . But where were Lalla Zaleha and Lalla Keltoum? Hafida responded evasively and unwillingly: she thought Zaleha was supervising the kitchen women's cooking, and Keltoum was assisting her.

A plateful of hardboiled eggs was served with pepper, salt and ground cumin. This was the usual beginning of a Ramadan supper. A shadow of discontent flew over our host's face as he peeled the egg: a tiny drop of yolk emerged from the coagulated white.

'I am awfully sorry,' he said. 'The eggs are not fully boiled.'

Lalla Hafida clapped her hands and darted a threatening glance towards the door — and towards a whip hanging beside it. Only she knew how to keep order in this house. As for Zaleha . . .

The eggs were immediately removed, and a tureen of milk soup, which reminded me of the Estonian variety, with barley, was brought in its place. The soup was eaten from individual bowls, using brand-new dipper-shaped lemontree spoons bought specially for Ramadan. The master of the house ate in a leisurely fashion, uttering few words. He was fully given over to culinary enjoyment. Hafida did not partake of the meal: the women usually ate separately later. She sat with her hands in her lap, and at times watched her husband long and penetratingly. Apart from brief responses to some of our questions she did not speak.

A *tajine* followed, a beef and carrot stew. When the servant lifted the cover of the clay dish, steam escaped, and the sauce continued to bubble at the edges. Again our host glanced in the direction of the door, and a servant rushed in to execute his wordless wish. To cool the dish, a towel was waved and flapped above our heads as if to scatter imaginary flies. Beans with mutton was the next dish, and the supper concluded with fruits of the current winter season: oranges and mandarins. Hadj Kadur did not touch them, and slipping away from the table he quickly stuffed cotton in his ears and nostrils.

'I have a pimple in my nose,' he explained. 'The acid aroma of the fruit is said to be very bad for it and could make it fester.'

The table was carried out, and we washed our hands. The *tbib* turned to the host and asked:

'How do you feel during the first days of the fast?'

'Medium, thanks be to Allah. At first the fasting weakens you, of course, but the later effect is positive. The stomach gets a month-long rest, since one does not want to eat as much at night as during the day. Many a person may thus get rid of his disease.'

'Oh yes,' the *tbib* agreed, 'provided that the fast is carried out quietly, including a nightly rest. However, this strange night life with visits and cardplaying which last till dawn . . .'

'The fast is what it is, and whatever belongs to it is good,' the master of the house corrected the *tbib*. 'Fasting helps to redeem our sins and has done so since the world was created.'

'Since the world was created?' the *tbib* marvelled. 'Wasn't Prophet Mohammed the one who established the fast of Ramadan?'

'It goes back to the creation of the world,' Hadj Kadur replied emphatically 'Or do you think Sidi Adam had no sins to expiate so that he did not need to fast? In fact, he was the very person to whom the angel Gabriel appeared with the command to fast for three days. You see, after expulsion from Paradise Adam's body was dark and hairy. But what happened then? At the end of the first day of fast, one-third of his body surface became white and smooth. Another third did so on the second day, and on the third day his whole body was clear. All the prophets coming after Sidi Adam fasted, too — Sidna Moses and the rest of them.' He rubbed his toes with fingers, then continued eagerly:

'Yes, all the rest of them — Sidna Solomon and Sidna Jonah and Sidna Zechariah and Sidna John. You see, all together there have been 124,000 prophets; didn't you know this? In memory of Adam, the fast was called 'the white days' until the advent of prophet Sidna Jesus who fasted for forty days. But the last one, the prophet of the prophets, was ordered by God to fast for either thirty or twenty-nine days, as indicated by the moon in the sky. We follow this practice. Praised be the Almighty!'

A shift to worldly topics was advisable. The *tbib*, well aware of a particular passion of our host, turned the conversation to golf. Hadj Kadur's placid expression disappeared. He became almost boyishly lively:

'I'm doing well, in fact a bit too well. Yesterday I played with the pasha, and won!' Hadj looked a different person, laughing and telling how the pasha had hired a personal caddy direct from England, paying him 50,000 francs for two months' service and advice, and yet he had lost the game.

Lalla Hafida could not care less for golf. 'Sports' was for her an alien and hollow phrase. She leaned back against the cushions and yawned incessantly.

'Would it be possible to see Lalla Zaleha and Lalla Keltoum?' I asked her.

Hafida's yawn stopped abruptly half-way through. She replied curtly:

'They are tired.'

However, our attentive host had heard my inquiry. He called a servant and told her to call in the women. Aunt Yamina was the first to arrive with the child Rbib clinging to her skirt train. Three women I did not know followed, probably the master's relatives, but there was no sign of Zaleha or Keltoum. The strange women responded clumsily to our handshakes and tried to hide behind each other as they sat down.

'They are straight from the High Atlas and still a bit wild,' our host smiled. 'They are totally ignorant of European customs and feel embarrassed in your presence, *tbib*.'

Aunt Yamina was prostrate with awe towards the master; her head almost disappeared inside her yellow kerchief. Rbib sat quiet as a mouse in his blue taffeta gown. He turned his wide-open eyes towards Hadj Kadur, who was for him the supreme figure of power in the world. One of the women sat close to me. Suddenly the master rose and, supple as a cat, placed himself between us. Almost leaning on me with his back, he started a hushed conversation with the mountain woman. Lalla Hafida seized the occasion and whispered to the *tbib*:

'Did you bring the photos?'

The *tbib* nodded and pulled out his wallet, but the host suddenly turned round and asked:

'What's the matter?'

'Oh, nothing . . .' The *tbib* was just shuffling his money and documents . . . The host resumed his conversation. I purposely leaned against him and gave the *tbib* the signal for action. The pictures slipped into Hafida's palm, then immediately to the floor and under her caftan train. Hafida scowled at her husband and pondered. The master seemed in an excellent mood. One could take a risk. Decisively, Hafida handed one of the pictures to Aunt Yamina who sat opposite and had breathlessly followed what was going on. A quick grab, and Hadj Kadur had the picture in his hand.

'I developed them myself, and they will not go beyond this house,' the *tbib* tried to assuage the master's possible annoyance. Hadj Kadur inspected the photo and was satisfied:

'Well enough, if that's the way it is.'

Her tension released, Lalla Hafida felt like expressing her pleasure at the outcome in an active way. She produced a zither-like instrument out of a curtained window niche.

'It's called a *kannel*,' she explained and started pinching its strings. She touched them pensively and lightly at first, then suddenly burst into a virtuoso performance. A complex Arab tune arose from under her fingers, and the blizzard of sounds betrayed a gifted player — an artist stranded in Hadj Kadur's harem. The music electrified the bystanders. Already Aunt Yamina was swinging in the place where she stood like a snake facing a charmer, and flapping her arms against her side. And when the music changed to the tune of a well-known song, auntie sang.

Nothing could now prevent the other women from joining in. Fired by the music, they forgot their reticence and clapped their hands with the rhythm.

Still, where were Lalla Zaleha and Lalla Keltoum? How come that song and dance had not brought them in to join us? I found a pretext to leave the room. In the semi-darkness of the patio I ran into Rahel.

'Oh, greetings, Rahel. So you are here, too? How are Lalla Zaleha and Lalla Keltoum doing?'

Before she could answer I saw a small group in the furthest corner of the patio. Lalla Zaleha crouched on the ground, flanked by Lalla Keltoum and her aged mother. Zaleha's lips trembled; she was crying. I bent down:

'What's the matter? Are you ill?' Instead of a reply Zaleha pressed her kerchief against her face, and the sobbing shook her shoulders once more. Rahel whispered:

'She has a quarrel going with the stout one.'

'With Lalla Hafida? Why?'

'Ah, the same old childbearing issue. Lalla Hafida wants to upstage Zaleha at any cost and bear a child for Hadj Kadur. She thinks it's Zaleha's doing that she hasn't yet succeeded. This is why she harasses Zaleha, as you have probably noticed. Now she has begun spreading the word that Zaleha is putting anti-pregnancy drugs into her food and trying to bewitch her by coming to her couch in the dark of the night to make noises.' To demonstrate such behaviour, Rahel stooped and let loose a terrifying 'oooh!' Keltoum's mother gave a start and covered her eyes:

'Allaah! Allaah! I don't care for people living together in such conditions.'

She meant to go on, but glanced anxiously towards the lighted door and said no more. Instead, she put her hand on her daughter's shoulder, and the idea behind the gesture was clear: You, my daughter, are stuck in this house between two co-wives. Because of them, does your body have to remain barren and your breasts without milk?

I tried to divert Zaleha:

'You know, Zaleha, those photos I took on the roof, they are done. We passed them on to Hafida.'

Her reaction was the reverse of what I expected. She straightened herself, anger shone from her swollen eyes, and she exclaimed hoarsely:

'Why did you give her my picture? You must never do it! It's my picture. My own. Mine!' She sobbed hysterically and hid her head in her arms.

'Would you like me to get your photo back and bring it here?'

'No, no. That would not do,' Rahel soothed us. 'Let it be for the while. Come back tomorrow and see what you can do. But the photo cannot be left in Hafida's hands for too long. She might use it for witchcraft. The stout one cannot be trusted. She is capable of anything. Zaleha no longer feels she knows how to act or where to go in this house. Hafida keeps an eye on her every move. It is enough for Zaleha to stand in the patio so that her shadow falls on the wall, and immediately Hafida will notice and memorise the position of the shadow, especially the head. Then later she will come on the sly and use a piece of sheet metal to scrape the mortar from that spot on the wall so that Lalla Zaleha's beauty may wane forever.'

Returning indoors I saw that Lalla Hafida had moved and was now nearer to the door. She could not have succeeded in overhearing our conversation, because she pulled her head between her shoulders, stooped and announced that she felt a bit sick. The *tbib* recommended going to bed early during Ramadan. As we got up to go home, the master of the house offered to escort us. He ordered a servant to bring him a warm burnous, wrapped it round him, and pulled the hood over his head. The patio was deserted. Lalla Hafida who walked with us seemed to feel feeble. She rubbed her lower chest incessantly and sighed.

'Does it hurt?' the *tbib* asked. Yes and no . . . the Lalla was not sure how to answer.

In a moment the master of the house pushed his finger like a chisel under Hafida's breasts and burst into a loud laugh. Didn't he have eyes and ears? Didn't he know all about such women's illnesses and other tricks? Women in the same household were bound to bicker with each other, and how could his house be an exception? Jealousy about the husband was the cause, but that was good. It raised a man's worth and gave meaning to life. Hadj had three flowers blossoming in his house: a fiery peony, a frail rose, and a virtuous camomile. And the city was not short of other flowers: two thousand prostitutes, among whom the *chikhas* definitely ranked first. Although they were the most expensive, they were also the most refined and knew how to captivate one's mind with song and dance. Picking one of them as a concubine was accepted practice and an extremely pleasurable one.

We walked home through the teeming night life of Ramadan. Trading and eating went on in the bazaar, amid laughing and high spirits. Gramophones screeched. The younger men sat and talked in the cafés. Many a one headed off to a relative's house to wish him well during the fast or to spend some time playing cards. At our door Hadj Kadur bade us farewell, saying to the *tbib*:

'Let your wife come and visit us more often. Your household gives her too much work, and this is not good for a woman. Let her stay at our place for entire days. Let her eat and drink.'

We thanked him for his gracious offer. Hadj Kadur pulled his burnous hood further over his brow and departed in a direction diametrically opposite to his home.

THE MONTH OF RAMADAN

The Ramadan practices in Hadj Kadur's house were the same as in the other households of Marrakech. An old rule applied in this harem: the wives took turns supervising the meal preparation for two days in a row. Lalla Zaleha was right when she viewed the month of Sha'ban as the end of the good life. Under the new system meal-times shifted to peculiar hours: in the morning before cock-crow and in the evening no later than a minute or two after sunset. Housewives had to keep a sharp eye on timing. Whoever happened to sleep in beyond dawn was punished by an empty stomach till sunset.

The usual habit of sleeping late in the morning and then stretching oneself comfortably vanished from the harem.

Although they went to bed late, housewives had to get up again as early as three or four o'clock. Still bug-eyed from sleep, they staggered into the kitchen to supervise the servants. Of course, the city had many people with simple habits for whom leftover soup and some bread and tea would suffice that early in the morning. But in Hadj Kadur's house breakfast had to be exemplary even during Ramadan. The mint tea absolutely had to be accompanied by pancakes. Chickens were roasted on charcoal, meatballs were served, and all this was topped with a glass of black coffee which kept thirst at bay during the day. The mouth had to be rinsed so that the saliva was clean, and then one was ready for the wail of the city sirens announcing the ban on the least bit of food.

By this time Hadj Kadur had his prayer rug under his arm, and he set out towards the mosque where the *mouden*'s call could be heard from the tower:

'*Alla-ah akba-ar*! Allah is great. The night with its shadows is retreating, and the day with its blinding light is born. God is the mightiest of all. There is no other god but Allah, and Mohammed is His prophet. Come and pray! There is no god but Allah!'

In the harem, one day of fasting followed another, long and limp. During daytime the ladies of the house tried to get as much sleep as possible. The servants, too, succumbed continuously to sleep — after all, they were the ones who did all this nightly cooking and roasting. The tasks that were not indispensable could be postponed. The main thing was to make sure that the evening soup was on time, with beans and lentils properly cooked. The rest could wait. The wet mop in the servant girl's hand moved fitfully, leaving dry bands on the stone-flagged floor, and only Lalla Hafida's whip-cracking could incite the drowsy servants to do the laundry.

The second week of fasting had barely begun when Lalla Zaleha fell ill. She felt it was caused by her own negligence, because she had not worn her necklace charm against the *djnun*, the spirits, ever since her pre-fast trip to the baths where its chain had been broken.

One had to be cautious about the *djnun*. They had been created and put in this world at the same time as humans. People could be seen but the spirits could not. They resided underground, preferring the privies and sewage pits of houses. More of them were bad than were good. They were spiteful and vengeful by nature and caused disease and misfortune. One could never pronounce their true name — 'djinn' in the singular or 'djnun' in the plural — without causing them to rush in and do mischief. Therefore, they were only alluded to as 'Those Others'. One got used to them in childhood, reacting by wearing charms and trying not to irritate them by, say, pouring boiling water into sewage pits. Salt was another substance they disliked.

Lalla Zaleha had not been worried when her charm fell off her neck at the baths. Light-minded as she was, she had even dared to laugh when cradling the charm in her palm:

'So what? Who needs it during Ramadan, when Allah has enchained Those Others for the whole month, as long as it lasts? We don't have to be afraid of them.'

When the others looked at her, aghast at such hubris, she added in a more conciliatory vein: 'Well, I'm not talking about the twenty-seventh night of Ramadan, when Those Others are let loose for a couple of hours. We know how to protect ourselves during that time.'

In her shortsightedness Zaleha had considered only Those Others, forgetting the charm's neutralising effect against the evil eye, an inexcusable mistake. The evil eye is not absent from the house even during the fast. The co-wife's biting glance causes disease. . . .

It was too late now to be sorry. Sickness had taken hold of her body, stinging and burning in her lungs. It made her cough and ran riot in her head. Heat rashes drowned her skin in sweat.

Another factor complicated the situation: Hadj Kadur had gone on a business trip of several days into the mountains. Fortunately, Aunt Yamina was on hand. As the senior female she was given the task of bringing outside help against the malady. Proud of her emergence to a key role, Aunt Yamina rushed off to the *taleb*, the scholar who had the whole Koran memorised line by line.

The *taleb* wrote some words of the Holy Scripture on a piece of paper. Since the remuneration was not inconsiderable, he added a few dates brought from Mecca and even a pinch of Mecca sand. Aunt Yamina rolled the sheet up reverently and put the paper and sand grains in a tiny leather purse she had bought beforehand. The purse was later placed on Lalla Zaleha's chest, and in the evening when the household congregated near the sickbed to take their fast-time soup, Zaleha would try hard to suck at the stone-hard dates.

The expectations were not fulfilled, and during the night the disease became worse. In the morning it was decided to dispatch Shiban to the master's brother Sidi Sliman. When the old man returned, he had the *tbib* with him, on Sidi Sliman's orders.

'Bronchitis,' the *tbib* mumbled after examining the patient. 'Of course she caught it while bustling about in the cold of the night between the patio, the kitchen, and the chambers.'

The *tbib* stuck an injection needle into Lalla Zaleha's live flesh. Aunt Yamina wailed and invoked the saints, but Lalla Hafida's firm hand assisted the *tbib*. A sick co-wife had to be helped with medication — such was Allah's command. But why did it have to be a needle? Hafida instructed the *tbib*:

'One shot is enough. When Lalla Zaleha has recovered and got her strength back, then you can give her another. Meanwhile give her some medicine she can drink, something tasty and sweet.'

However, the *tbib* was stubborn: the very next day he was back with his needle.

According to the clock in the physician's home, the time was approaching 10 p.m. Although it was late, the patient's condition had to be checked once more. Off we went.

Djemaa el-Fna was deserted, except for some sellers of oranges in whose tents small acetylene lamps still flickered. The side-streets were quiet. The open portal of the mosque allowed us to see its pillars and rugs. An old beggar woman sitting at its threshold grabbed at my coat and showered us with her pleas. Their echoes carried far down on the narrow wall-enclosed alley.

It was dark in front of Hadj Kadur's house. I felt the door with my fingers: if it was not yet padlocked, Shiban would allow us inside. My finger slipped into the keyhole; no padlock was to be felt next to it. So I let the iron knocker fall on the door. With alarm, I did detect the padlock at the very same moment, in the middle of the door. Shiban had done his duty, and no earthly power other than his master would persuade him to reopen the door. But the loud bang of the knocker had spread through the house.

'Who is it?' Lalla Hafida asked in suspicious tones on the other side of the door.

'It's me, the *tbib*. How's the sick one doing?'

Lalla Hafida did not respond. She must have been wondering why the *tbib* had come at such a late hour . . . I joined in:

'I am here too. We came to check on the patient before it's completely night. Is she asleep?'

Lalla Hafida's voice became at once direct and businesslike:

'Yes, she is asleep. She is feeling better.'

A few more instructions were passed through the keyhole, and then we both said good-bye in a very loud voice, so that it should be clear to Shiban that the male *tbib* had not come alone but with his wife. We turned back home. Clouds masked the moon and an icy breath from the Atlas was abroad. I shuddered and pulled my coat tighter around me.

Lalla Zaleha's recovery progressed at a good pace, and the resulting joy was reflected in the servants' faces. But when Hashouma received me in the hallway, her mouth was full not only of smiles but also bread. I looked at her in astonishment, since it was broad daylight on a fasting day. She exclaimed:

'I am now allowed to eat for seven days in a row, because I'm menstruating.'

'Aren't you jealous?' I teased Zohra, who was not yet in her teens. Her lips drew into a smile, and she boasted:

'In a few days I will start to eat too. I'm no longer a baby! But the men, they will not get a single day off. They'll have to keep fasting day after day, and so will old women — Aunt Yamina included.'

Chuckling, they were off to the kitchen hallway where the tiny

Rbib was peering out — he was munching something. Aunt
Yamina came from the kitchen, handed Rbib some black olives,
and stroked his head:

'Eat, little child. You are not yet subject to God's fasting
command. Your time will come, when you'll have to follow the
path of all the faithful.'

I found Lalla Zaleha sitting among cushions on her wide daytime couch. Hating the cold, she covered her head and torso with a
kerchief. There was a melancholy look in her wide eyes. Lalla
Hafida was with her: a sick person could never be left alone.
Sitting cross-legged on the rug, Hafida was hand-operating a sewing machine at a remarkable speed. She had placed it on a low
stool. A pile of curtain-like white fabric was spread on the ground
next to her.

The neighbour's wife was also there. Her front door was close
to Hadj Kadur's. All house fronts on the street were joined, but
the length of the outer wall of each house and the appearance of
the door gave an indication of the owner's wealth or his lack of it.
Hadj Kadur's neighbour was a market shopkeeper; his wall was
short and his door was of crude hatchetwork, but his wife seemed
able and well-behaved — someone suitable for an occasional invitation to the harem for plucking chickens when a bevy of male
guests unexpectedly flooded the house. In ordinary times the
neighbourly interaction was limited to an exchange of greetings
between Hashouma and the neighbour's servant when both were
on their way to the city baking oven with their load of bread
loaves.

However, Lalla Zaleha being sick made a courtesy call manda-
tory, and so the neighbour's wife came, leaving the servant to take
care of her children and of the fasting soup simmering on charcoals. Here she was now, her hands in her lap, silent and meek.

I tried to convince Zaleha:

'You should take some food to get yourself going. You know
that the Koran permits sick ones to eat in daylight too.'

Zaleha shook her head defensively. She would continue fasting.
She had fasted throughout her sickness and would carry on. Life
and death depended on Allah. She was even taking the cough medi-

cine only during the night. It was lucky that the *tbib*'s medication used injections, thus by-passing the mouth and not jeopardising Ramadan . . .

'The *tbib* will come and see you in the evening.'

The patient's eyes lighted up: the news made her happy. Lalla Hafida uttered a resounding '*ouakha!*' (good!) and whirred on with her sewing. I addressed her:

'How is the fast coming on?'

Hafida threw her head back heavily:

'No problems. Hadj Kadur's house isn't a poor one, is it? In the mornings and evenings we eat good food, and plenty of it!'

Only now did Lalla Keltoum come out from her boudoir, looking quite sleepy.

'Keep up the fast, Lalla!'

Keltoum wrinkled her nose and sighed tragicomically. She bent over herself on the sitting mattress, withdrawing her arms from the wide caftan sleeves and pressing them against her chest so that the sleeves hung empty. She yawned.

There was no way of getting the conversation going. None of them had the will or energy to exchange words, preoccupied as they were with the thought of food during such a miserable slow-flowing late afternoon. Zaleha was stretched out; her eyes were closed. Keltoum disengaged her left hand from underneath the caftan. Yawning incessantly, she pressed the back of her hand against her mouth so that the hollow of her palm could repel Satan. Each yawn ended with a muttered '*Astaghfar Allah!*' — I beg God's pardon. The sewing machine whirred on.

The neighbour's wife got up and left.

Zaleha's chamber was so different from Hafida's. No *bric-à-brac* here. The room's ancient classic Arab simplicity reflected the owner's sense of beauty. Soft-coloured tile panels lined the white walls. A simple white curtain surrounded Zaleha's marital bed at the far end of the chamber. A mountain rug with its reverse side turned out because of Ramadan could not hide its red-and-yellow gaiety. A few moth-holes in the red door curtain glimmered like stars with the bright light in the courtyard.

A room in the harem . . . Complete with the harem ladies

sitting right in front of me . . . Without fountains or roses. And even if the house had been a princely one, they would still have been suffering from empty stomachs during the fast.

I tried to imagine them in modern surroundings, each fulfilling her natural abilities, Lalla Hafida as a choir director and Lalla Zaleha as a contributor to a women's journal. But Lalla Keltoum? Here I was puzzled, for where would she fit in? This young being who hid herself behind the other spouses remained an enigma. Was it a case of still waters running deep?

In the harem their lives fused together. From morning to evening, without a break, they shared the same surroundings; one of them could not take a single step without the others knowing. This was something they had got used to. Yet each one of them was, and remained to the others, a *darra* — an additional wife.

When the daughter of the Prophet Mohammed (may Allah elevate him!) first saw her *darra*, she spat on the ground. The oleander bush, the *defla*, sprouted from this holy saliva. It has gorgeous clusters of blossoms but the juice from its stem is bitter. Hence the saying: '*Darra marra kif defla*' — an additional wife is bitter like the oleander.

And what was the name for thistles by the roadside and in the fields? *Darra*, again. At times a derisive ditty was hummed:

> If a darra became a habiba [female friend],
> then a leffa [viper] will become a tbiba [healer].

Hadj Kadur's spouses remained oleanders for each other, flowery on the surface and bitter internally. What they had in common was the very drive that drove them apart: this was the desire to rank first in the master's eyes, their common master who came home only to eat and rest, who never gave any account of his doings outside the house or of his plans for the future, and who did not comprehend the possibility of the interfusion of two souls. So what did those three spouses expect from Hadj Kadur in concrete terms? What they expected was, of course, a child.

In this joint child-getting marathon, no one in the family would even for a moment consider the possibility that the master of the house, still an agile runner even now, had dissipated his potency back in the days of his youth and had thus forfeited his chances for the medal. No, in each woman's opinion her barrenness was always the work of the other wife — by her envy and black magic.

While Allah and Islam ruled the humans, another secretive and autonomous power lurked about in the world: the occult power. In times of mental agony one could resort to it either by attracting the power for one's own benefit or for deflecting its effects when one had to defend oneself.

Magic: medicine for the soul.

Lalla Hafida continued to sew enthusiastically. She was hemming a pile of white cloth with red and blue lace.

'What is it you are making?' I inquired.

'A mosquito net for the couch.'

'For yourself?' — 'For myself.'

'But I see you are making two of them.'

· Hafida did not deign to answer, but Zaleha rocked herself on her couch, shook her head quietly, and observed:

'There's only one house and only one mosquito net in the house. Lalla Hafida alone has to have a net. The other one she's sewing is for Hadj Kadur's brother's house.'

Did Lalla Hafida show anger? Her face stayed calm, but when Zaleha left the room somewhat later, sliding her feet, Hafida said something to Keltoum which, to me, seemed disparaging of Zaleha.

Someone knocked at the house door. A loud conversation was heard from the street. Hashouma came to announce that Rahel the Jewess had arrived with some merchandise: shawls. Any interest?

'Just bring them in!' Hafida commanded.

When the servant returned, Hafida took the whole batch and set them on her lap. She picked out one that suited her with amazing speed. She briskly cast it over her head, and producing a small mirror from her pocket, peered into it.

'How much are they?' she asked.

'The old woman is asking ten francs . . .'

'Five!' Lalla Hafida countered, and her nostrils widened menacingly. The whole of her massive body and the way she stretched her head forward gave a signal: she would not yield an inch.

'Five!' she repeated and threw a five-franc bill at Hashouma's feet. The servant picked it up and went to bargain at the door, the shawls still hanging on her arm.

'The crone insists on six francs,' she announced when she came back.

'Five!' Hafida repeated again, and bent over her work. A few minutes later the servant, humbly and somewhat fearfully, placed the bank note on her mistress's knee: the Jewess had rejected the offer.

Hafida continued to sew. The piece she had in her hand now was a salmon-pink gown for Rbib, designed to be worn at the end-of-fast festivities. She embroidered the collar with a black woollen band.

'That's nice!' Keltoum approved in a somnolent voice, and even Lalla Zaleha nodded assent.

The sun was leaving the patio, and the seamstress shifted herself and her machine closer to the door. Time passed, and the room was getting darker. The wheel of the machine kept turning. Aunt Yamina came from the kitchen, with her hands wet, and sat down; she smelled of fresh mint, which she had been cleaning for the tea. Agitation seized Zaleha and Keltoum. They stretched themselves and hesitated. Wasn't it a smell of roast meat flowing in from the kitchen, that captious sweet aroma spreading out and making one salivate?

Lalla Hafida also drew those kitchen aromas into her nostrils, and suddenly her stately firmness collapsed. She threw the boy's pink gown to the other end of the room and cried out impulsively: 'Eat! I want to eat!' Having been so haughty only a few minutes ago, she had lost self-control.

THE NIGHT OF FATE

The twenty-seventh night of Ramadan was upon us: *Laylat el-Kdar* or the Night of Fate — the night during which a person's entire course of life is predetermined for the whole ensuing year. It is the holiest of all nights, since the angel Gabriel, envoy of God, revealed himself to Mohammed in Mecca on that night. Hovering two arrowshot-lengths above the ground, Gabriel dictated the everlasting words of the Koran's first *sura*: 'Read in the name of your Lord who created man out of curdled blood. Read!'

The Koran bears witness: 'We have revealed the Koran on the Night of Fate, the incomparable and marvellous night, the favoured one among thousands of nights. Everywhere, at God's command, the spirits and the angels are near. Pray, and repeat your prayers till dawn.'

At the onset of darkness Hadj Kadur, along with all other male residents of the city, hurried off to follow God's command. The bright lights of the thirty-four mosques and hundred and seven lesser shrines of Marrakech invited them: let everyone come and meet to commemorate the birth of the Holy Book and to honour the sole and indivisible God. Turn your face towards Mecca and repeat devoutly throughout the night the fervent rhythmic *suras* which announce God's truth. Ponder till dawn Allah's mercy and His immeasurable power over you, and hope for the salvation of your soul and for eternal life in Paradise.

As he made his way to the mosque, Hadj Kadur felt a slight pang of fear. What if he happened to drop off to sleep even for a single second during the long night ahead that he would have to pass on the prayer carpet? If he did, all his wishes for the coming year might remain unfulfilled, since there is only a single short period during that night when God in the heaven will listen to the supplication of a believer in a state of ecstatic alert.

Women, of course, stayed at home. Their task was different from that of the men, but it was no less important. Didn't the Book say 'Everywhere spirits and angels are near'? Who were the spirits who did not belong to the angelic kind? Those Others, of course. Throughout the month of Ramadan they stayed chained, but during the coming night this mostly evil element would be released entirely for a few hours — the chiefs of spirits, those horrible *afarits*, and the myriad of smaller *djnun* under their command. The women were to prevent those demons from intruding

into the houses. Their principal means were fumigating the house
with potent compounds and keeping up the nightly vigil.

Hadj Kadur's brother Sidi Sliman was left in charge of the
harem. His proper place would also have been in the mosque, but
the women protested strongly at the idea of being left without the
presence of a single male. Who could say what ghastly events
might occur during such a night?

Aunt Yamina was dispatched early in the day to buy the
fumigating materials at the Djemaa el-Fna. The task proved a
pleasant one. What clamour and gaiety engulfed the great square!
It had turned into an enormous fairground packed with crowds.
Long lines of women and men squatted in front of their merchandise, offering toys as gifts for children. Women sold little painted
drums and men various factory-made goods: whistles, toys and
balloons. The air was full of the clatter of toys and the beating of
drums. Huge piles of special Night of Fate honey cakes glittered
on the tables: intricate golden grease flowers with wide petals
which promised to fill one's mouth with aromatic juice when
crunched by the teeth later in the evening. Business was most brisk
for the sellers of fumigation herbs, since their tables did not cater
for the children's fun or the adults' taste buds but offered very
serious and much-needed merchandise. Box after box bulged with
myrrh and incense, various kinds of resins, crystals, seeds, and also
small pieces of sandalwood.

Aunt Yamina was a connoisseur. She knew which smells had
the effect of repelling the *djnun* while being pleasant to humans. So
she carefully chose a combination of seven compounds: white and
black incense, myrtle blossoms and rose leaves, coriander seeds,
aloe resin, and lavender. The expensive sandalwood was bought
by the master himself, as were the main holiday gifts: caftans for
the ladies and, without fail, new footwear for the whole household, not forgetting the servants.

Aunt Yamina did not buy any cakes. The master disdained the
kinds one bought from a fairground, and could order his directly
from an experienced baker. But Aunt Yamina did add to her bag a
few toys for the children, Bubkir and Rbib.

As soon as the sun had set, the fumigating began. This

momentous task demanded absolute silence on the part of those carrying it out, as well as onlookers. The herbs in the hot chafing dish were entrusted to Hashouma, the head servant. Lalla Hafida walked ahead, with compressed lips and an enigmatic expression on her face. She led the servant from one room to another and pointed to every corner into which Those Others could slip and which therefore had to receive a good whiff of smoke. The kitchen, the water container stand in the hall, and especially the lavatory and the sewage drain had to get plenty. Even the flat roof received its share, since the sweetish odour from inside the house rose through the patio and mixed with the smoke from the neighbours' houses into a single demon-repellent cloud hovering over the entire city.

Night was at hand. The eight of us held vigil in Lalla Hafida's chamber, sitting in a circle along the walls. Two men were with the women: Sidi Sliman and the *tbib*. Two long candlesticks, each holding a thick, burning candle, stood on the carpet at opposite ends of the room. In the centre the smell of sandalwood issued from a capsule for burning incense. Its brass support was placed over charcoal.

The learned *talebs*, the Koranic scholars, had calculated that spirits could make their appearance between the nocturnal hours of eleven and three. The clock hand dragged towards midnight. Were the *djnun* already circling above our heads? We sat silently in positions of sharp attention, waiting for some noise from the outside or even — Allah forbid! — some visible apparition.

Through the door curtain one could see the blurred cluster of servants, who had gathered in the patio before the chamber. They huddled together like sheep. The patio was not completely dark, since there a candle flickered too, protected by a sowing tray and casting shadows of fluctuating depth on the walls. The other rooms also had candles, even upstairs. The house had plenty of electric bulbs, but they were not to be used; only the holy candles possessed the power to repel the evil powers.

Everyone felt scared. The lightly-built Sidi Sliman, the harem's protector and rescuer, tried to explain in a soft voice that no demon's tooth could attack a truly pious person, but he did not look entirely convinced by his own claim.

The sandalwood gave off a sweet aroma. The room already smelled so strong that our clothes and even our hair were impregnated. Isolated strands of smoke escaped from the incense container, joining overhead in a single circling column which diffused and wrapped the greyish chamber in a still denser haze. The flicker of candles blurred the faces. Sidi Sliman's eye sockets were sombre. Lalla Ftuh's noseless face became an unearthly mask. Aunt Yamina sat as if on needles, restless and incessantly keeping a watchful eye on the patio.

There was a woollen cushion under me and another supporting my back, and I began to float somewhere on the outskirts of reality when Lalla Hafida's voice startled us from the daze. She shouted to the kitchen crone behind the curtain:

'Hannem, did you take the couscous to the roof terrace? You didn't by any chance add salt, did you?'

'Yes, Lalla. No, Lalla. I crushed some sugar and spread it on the dish and also around it.'

'For whom is this couscous intended?' I asked.

'For Those Others,' Hafida explained. 'We act wisely in trying to please them. Sugar is something they seem to like.'

But now another thought made Zaleha rise from the couch at the other end of the chamber. She questioned me excitedly:

'Listen, do you by any chance have a black rooster in your house during this night?'

'And suppose I do?'

Zaleha became upset: 'You do? We'll send Sliman right away to slaughter it!'

I reassured everyone present that there was no rooster in my house, and every corner of the place had been carefully fumigated by my servant. I summoned up the courage to ask Sidi Sliman:

'Was your fumigation last year a success?'

The master's brother shifted a bit, temporised, and replied: '*Shuyya.*'

The Moroccan Arabic '*shuyya*' has a superb ability to adjust itself to any situation. It can mean: 'very little', 'a little', 'medium', 'quite a bit', 'rather extensively', and even 'soon'. It stays within the bounds of politeness, fits everywhere, and saves one from getting stuck in a tight corner. It requires no further elaboration, but Sidi Sliman none the less added:

'Well, one could sense the presence of Those Others here and there during the year, but they have not done any mischief.'

'Have you yourself seen them?'

Sidi shifted on the couch, dodging this direct question. He had something on his mind, but he could not find the right words. Unexpectedly I found myself under attack by Lalla Ftuh:

'You there! Do you believe in the existence of Those Others?'

Now I was in a corner. If I said 'no' I would contradict the truth of the Koran and the Bible, and my prestige would suffer. Yet they would not take a 'yes' on my part at face value either. In imitation of Sidi Sliman's 'shuyya', I chose the golden mean: 'Personally I have not encountered any of them.'

'Well', Lalla Zaleha commented, 'if you had been visiting us the night the Berber taleb Ambarek was here, then both of you would have been convinced of their existence.'

'I'll tell you about it myself!' Lalla Hafida straightened herself. 'That's a man from the other side of the mountains who claims to be related to Them. Hadj Kadur brought him to our house. Allah preserve us! The deeds he did!'

'Tell them about those serpents,' Auntie Yamina slipped in, but with an angry glance Hafida silenced the interruptor:

'All in good time!' she snapped provocatively. 'Why should I start with the serpents? Did they come first? Well, did they?' And when Aunt Yamina kept quiet: 'So, why make such a stupid interruption?'

She leaned back against the cushion and began:

'That man was sitting in this room, right where you are sitting, facing the door,' and she pointed at me. 'The master, Sidi Sliman, and three other male relatives were with him. The women insisted that my room be used because that way we could stand in the patio, behind the curtain, and take in what was happening. When the men had finished their tea, Ambarek asked for the tray to be put down in front of him. He covered it with a cloth, then suddenly, in the middle of the conversation, he pulled the cloth away, and I can tell you — our eyes stared. The tray was heaped with gorgeous fruit the like of which you have never seen: apples and oranges as large as the head of that boy Rbib. Hadj Kadur even tasted one of them. Then Ambarek passed the cloth over the tray, and the fruit was gone. What do you make of that?'

We had nothing to say, and Hafida continued: 'Let me now tell you what happened next. The man took off his red Turkish hat, put it on the floor, and again used the cloth to cover it. Spellbound, we looked at it. The man whisked the cloth off, and do you know what we saw on the rug?' Hafida spread her arms wide, and her eyes protruded from their sockets:

'Snakes! A whole brood of snakes writhing on the floor! Allah, how we screamed! Even Hadj Kadur shrank back, and the others were frozen with terror. The master exclaimed: 'Remove those snakes!' The *taleb* swept his cloth high over the snakes, and they vanished instantly. Those Others grabbed them at once and took them away.'

'Oh yes,' Sidi Sliman interjected, rather sheepishly as if apologising for having shown fear. 'Yes, that was no joke. Snakes can kill.'

'*Besmellah rahman rahim* — in the name of the merciful and graceful Allah,' Lalla Ftuh whispered kissing her palms, and all those in the room repeated the formula to repel evil. But Lalla Hafida was not yet through:

'Ambarek let Those Others do still more tricks. He took the master's pocket watch in his hand. And then at once the watch was in the hand of that kitchen hag Hannem standing next to me in the patio. Hannem looked at it, wondering what on earth she had taken out of the kitchen. When she realised there was gold glittering there in her hand, she cried out and let it go. You'd think the watch would have fallen on the ground floor and broken? Not a bit of it! At the very same moment it was back inside the room, perched on the master's knee. Tell me, *tbib*, why are foreigners so unreasonable and obstinate that they don't admit to the existence of Those Others?'

The *tbib* shook his shoulders. There was no point in telling this audience about hypnosis.

The talk about malevolent beings increased everyone's anxiety. The room fell silent. Shadows from the candlelight wavered on the ceiling. The eyes of the servants in the patio flashed catlike.

The kettle near the chamber door began to hum. The tea water was boiling. Lalla Keltoum signalled towards the door opening. Zohra set the tray with glasses in front of Keltoum, whose fingers trembled as she dropped the tea leaves into the teapot. When Zohra tilted the kettle, she proved so unusually clumsy that the stream of hot water almost touched Keltoum's hand instead of going into the pot!

We waited for the tea to brew. One of the candles started to crackle, and grease flowed down its side. Lalla Hafida — energetically shouting *'Sidi Rabbi!'* — rose, bent over the candle, and moistened her fingers to snuff it.

At this very moment a crash in the patio sent cold shivers down our spines. A metallic rumble followed. Everyone in the room looked thunderstruck, ready to jump to their feet, but still frozen with terror. The servants out in the patio screamed. Aunt Yamina squealed piercingly, crumpled up on the floor, and hid her head between the handrests of the couch.

'Allah! Allah, besmellah rahman rahim!' Lalla Hafida mumbled, her lips pale. Then, resolutely, she proceeded to recite a prayer. The others joined in, shakily at first but then, finding mutual encouragement, more fluently and intelligibly. Aunt Yamina alone stayed bundled against the couch, apparently crazed with fear.

'All right now, what could it have been?' said the *tbib*, getting to his feet. 'It seems to me that something must have fallen. . . .' He pushed the door curtain aside, and stepped into the patio. Soon we heard his hearty laughter:

'Hey, your large round brass tray is on the ground. Wasn't it leaning against the wall earlier?'

'Certainly it was,' the cook could be heard answering in a half-choked voice. 'But I saw myself how Those Others brought it down.'

'Oh, Those Others? Now did you actually see them pushing the tray?'

'W-ell, no, I did not quite see them, but who else . . .'

'Then what are you talking about, if you did not quite see them? You always have 'Those Others' doing this and 'Those Others' doing that. Why can't a tray slip when it has been placed against the wall, and the floor it is standing on is well polished? That's something Moroccan trays do all the time.' So the *tbib* argued as he returned to the chamber.

His triumphant stand made everyone breathe easier. Even Sidi Sliman, sticking out his chest, gesticulated and raised his voice, trying to prove to the women that their fears were groundless.

'Why aren't you pouring the tea?' Hafida suddenly demanded of Keltoum, as if she had been the cause of the delay.

Tea caused everyone's confidence to come back. By the time the second glass had been gulped down, all agitation had subsided. Already some humorous comments were crackling in the air. Only Aunt Yamina had not yet recovered. Deaf to every entreaty, she still lay hiding her face.

This gave Hafida a good opportunity to amuse the others. She tiptoed close to Aunt Yamina and uttered an unearthly cry, at the same time swishing her heavy hand at her. Aunt Yamina scrambled to her feet with a cry. She was about to make a frantic dash into the patio when the laughter of the others brought her to her senses.

'For shame!' she hissed through clenched teeth. 'Scaring a believer in such a way! May Allah punish you for doing such a thing!'

Hafida took umbrage. 'Shut up!' she roared and threw out her chin. 'Don't give her any tea,' she added, turning to Keltoum, 'let her go without.'

Lalla Zaleha rose, went to the tray and, picking up a glass, took it to Aunt Yamina. As she passed Hafida, her glance seemed to say, in defiance of her co-wife: do you think you are the only one here to give orders?

When everyone had calmed down, I repeated my earlier question to Sidi Sliman:

'Have you seen Those Others with your own eyes?'

After the recent scare, the man was prepared to let go some of his reserve:

'Yes indeed, I once did, may Allah protect me!'

'Where?'

'Inside an old house. It was my house, but it was dilapidated and nobody lived in it. Only I, and no one else, had the key. One evening I was passing by and I noticed a glimmer of light inside. Who had dared to go in without my permission? I thought with dismay, also wondering how they got in. I turned the key, walked across the patio to the lighted room, and banged the door open. I still shudder when I think of what I saw. An open fire was blazing in the middle of the empty floor, and crouching around it were three hideous faceless and hairy dark creatures. The thought flashed through my mind that they weren't human. I had hardly gone back one step when one of the spirits stretched out an arm to seize me — it was terribly long. I shrank away from it, dashed out into the street like a madman, and ran to the nearby mosque. How I ever reached home later I don't know. And I sold the house — I didn't want to have anything to do with it after that.'

'Who bought it?'

'Some unknown Berber. He still lives there, and I haven't heard anything about spirits. That isn't surprising because I got a *taleb* to fumigate the house heavily inside and outside. However, there are houses where no one can get rid of the demons. Take that house in Dabash Street next to the barber Lakhsen: it's a good property, there's nothing wrong with it, but no one can live there. Every night a black lamb rises from the well, bleating sadly, and . . .'

Sidi Sliman stopped there in mid-sentence, raised his head, and listened open-mouthed. Noises from the street came into the patio: there were wheels rolling on the rough surface, a cart was being hauled, and men were talking. Lalla Hafida commanded Sidi Sliman:

'Go and see what's going on. Go right away, as you have the key.'

The husband's brother got up reluctantly, went to the hall, and opened the door. Like a flock of sparrows the servants followed and looked over his shoulder. The noise had stopped by the neighbour's door. A woman wrapped in a *haik* stood beside the cart out of which a large red wooden chest was being lowered. A bridal chest! Everyone immediately knew what it meant: the neighbour was bringing home a new wife, the first additional one.

The news hit those gathered in the chamber like a bombshell. They rose, ran into the patio, and moved about excitedly exchanging whispered comments: 'what nerve on the neighbour's part, to bring a new wife home on the very Night of Fate and, moreover, during the dangerous hour of the *djnun*! And who was that woman? Could it even be a *djinniyya*, a female spirit, who had assumed a human body and face?

The Night of Fate, the assignment of fates . . . Lalla Hafida shuddered. Could it now be precisely the supreme moment in the night when one could offer one's wishes to God? 'Let's pray!' she called out and prostrated herself on her prayer rug. Her prayer was short and to the point, and within a short time, what she had prayed for would be revealed: 'Lord, I wish that Hadj Kadur will give me permission, at the end-of-the-fast celebrations, to adopt a baby as my child.'

A somewhat similar plea arose from the depths of Lalla Zaleha's heart, but in quiet and total submission to God's will.

Keltoum slipped behind the door curtain of her chamber. She felt as if a rope were throttling her. Instead of words of prayer, these other ones came to her lips — dreadful and alluring words of magic which she had to chisel into her mind in order to assert her good fortune and her master's love at the coming feast:

> *I tie you down against a hundred women and two women,*
> *against a hundred women in motley veils,*
> *against a hundred slave girls,*
> *against a hundred young men in vests.*

The *djnun*, who happened to be circling the house at that very moment, overheard Lalla Keltoum's mysterious silent pleas. Their malicious mocking sounded like the rattle made by the neighbour's cart-wheels before they flew off in search of further prey elsewhere.

EL-AID EL-FITR: THE END OF THE FAST

El-Aid el-Fitr is the feast marking the end of the fast. On that morning the sun radiated a special holiday mood. Peace and calm were spread over the city. Obligations had been fulfilled, accounts with God had been settled.

Groups of men in chalk-white robes congratulated each other in the streets on the successful execution of the fast. They prepared for the noonday worship. What an experience it was to pray together, at precisely the same time as everyone else in the city, at the same time as all the millions of Moroccan men, and using exactly the same words in the same prayer sequences! And they knew as well that the seven hundred million Muslims around the globe would join in, all using the same Arabic lines from the Koran regardless of what their native language might be. In principle they would all do it simultaneously although the journeys of the sun and the moon would mean that the hands of the clocks would be in different positions in different countries. Every man's breast was bursting with thanks to Allah for being allowed to be part of the *umma*, the united Muslim community of those who knew bliss in this world.

Oh, women! Your knowledge of the Koran is scanty — almost non-existent, in fact — because unlike the boys you have not spent your childhood days in the Koran school, struggling from morning to evening to memorise the mighty *suras* of the Holy Book.

But do not worry. The men's prayers will sanctify you too. Go about your business, matrons and house servants! Send the children to sleep, get the kitchen bellows going to light up the charcoal, crush pepper and coffee beans in your mortars. Your skills and your experience will conjure a feast on the table for those returning from the mosque, and the excitement and charm you create will fill the house and the mind with wellbeing.

But what was wrong in Hadj Kadur's home? Why were the ladies of the house all so downcast and sullen? Why did the servants move around haltingly, indifferent to their tasks?

This is what happens with the world's might and glory. While raising up some, it presses others to the ground. A great honour had befallen Hadj Kadur. The pasha had taken him along to Rabat, as a member of the Marrakech delegation which would present the holiday gift, a golden dagger decorated with jewels, to the honoured and beloved monarch, Mohammed the Fifth. God preserve the effulgence of his glory!

However, for Hadj Kadur's spouses the master's absence had threatened to turn the Great Feast into an insignificant day. What pleasure can there be in putting on glittering new robes and in making oneself up enticingly for the first time in a month, when the husband will not be there to brush you approvingly with his glance? And how could there be any mood of excitement in a placid house without guests?

The sombre mood was lightened a little by getting out the cosmetic paraphernalia that had been hidden away for the whole duration of the fast. It was pleasant to rub one's gums again with a piece of walnut wood that turned them reddish-brown, setting off the flashing white of the teeth. The fast-time pallor of the face yielded to rouge, and the face itself looked fuller. The mouth lighted up with a bright red. But eyes were the main thing. How wonderful it felt to grab a metal or wooden *merroud* containing the kohl eyeliner. This black powder was carefully prepared on certain nights when there was a moon, using charcoal made of oleander roots, and with the addition of nutmeg, aloe, hedgehog and eagle bile, and one indispensable fly. You dip a small stick in the *merroud* and apply the eyeliner to the edges of your lids — and it's magical how that dark frame makes the eyes flash with liveliness and promises. While making up, one had good reason to hum:

> *I darkened my eyes.*
> *Whoever sees me will madden with desire . . .*

But he whom one might seduce was not at home. Even Allah could not grant the pleas heard during the Night of Fate if the master was away.

Lalla Hafida tried to soothe the household's disappointment, or at least her own, by means of her ever-present energy. During the morning she sat in the hall and, assisted by Shiban, distributed barley to supplicants coming to the door. This was according to the command of the holy Koran. Later, she surprised the others by proposing an unauthorised evening in the master's room.

The ladies could not complain of being completely abandoned. The *tbib* and his wife came to visit, and of course the master's brother was present. Sidi Sliman had even brought his short, stout wife. The lady had provocative make-up and pursed lips. Her head seemed to rest on her double chin and, in conformity with good manners, she did not utter a word. Boredom lurked on her husband's face, along with a hint of awkwardness: so now you had to sit there and chaperone these three 'widows' while your own household, children, and friends were waiting for you at home . . .

Being in the most hallowed place in the house inevitably made the household members self-conscious. The sitting mattresses lining the walls seemed excessively high, and the striped silken covers had a sleek, cold feeling about them. The large red carpet laid in the space between the seats was too immaculate. The brass rods of a European-style bed across the end of the room had a smart glitter but seemed out of place. A mirror covered the wall above the bed, doubling the visual length of the room: thus the sitting mattresses seemed to stretch twice their actual length, and the number of cushions on them appeared prodigious. How many of them actually were there? No fewer than twenty-four large ones leant against the wall and fourteen small ones on top of them, all made of spangled velvet and brocade. The electric candelabrum cast sharp rays on the cedarwood ceiling high above us.

An antique gramophone was set on the carpet in our midst. Its huge funnel reared up like the neck of an antediluvian beast. But despite its enormous size it produced only high squeaky sounds.

Lalla Hafida changed the record, and then walked around wondering what else to do to amuse the guests. She looked nervous and out of humour. Lalla Zaleha, frail but graceful and elegant in her light blue caftan, observed Hafida with a faint smile: let her co-wife bustle and boss around — it wouldn't affect her. Let that other one rush around the room in her garish red gown, stout and feeling important . . .

Aunt Yamina was nodding off. After the long fast, and with

the master away, she was allowing herself the indulgence of a few grains of hashish. Hafida stopped in front of her — what a convenient target for her bad temper was that insignificant member of the household.

'Get up and dance!' she shouted. When Aunt Yamina balked drowsily, Hafida's anger flared up. A thick silken cord on her shoulders served to hold up the sleeves; Hafida seized it and lifted it up menacingly. Reluctantly Aunt Yamina rose, stretched herself, and began to move around lurching grotesquely. Okay, I will hop around for you, her grimaces seemed to say; look at me, if that is what you want, and see if I am attractive or not. I'll even roll my eyes — do you like that? Are you asking for more?

Hafida laughed loudly. As Aunt Yamina settled back on her seat, Hafida looked toward the door, where Zohra was crouching on the stairsteps waiting for orders.

'Zohra! You come and dance!'

Rosy-cheeked, brown-eyed Zohra obliged eagerly. Stopping for a moment in the middle of the room, she began to slide around on the carpet half-walking and half-skipping. Her troso was well balanced; the girl seemed to enjoy improvisation. A tiny kerchief tied her braids into a bundle at the back of her neck, revealing her smooth head. Zohra made her shoulders quiver, and the ends of her shawl and her silver earrings leaped up and down. Attractive Zohra, I mused, will you seduce the master of the house one day?

Perhaps the same thought crossed Hafida's mind. She frowned and called out almost crossly:

'That will do! Now bring Ms'ouda!'

The tiny kitchen girl in her soiled dress stood scared in the midst of her mistresses. Her hair was shaggy and shorn in odd patches. 'Dance!' Hafida ordered relentlessly. With a childlike shyness in her eyes, Ms'ouda obediently lifted her thin arms, kicked her legs awkwardly, and stumbled on the spot like a chained animal. Hafida gave up: 'Get lost!'

A smell of burned fat rose from the kitchen below. That meant that the kitchen women were grilling *kefta*, ground meat wrapped round a spit. The children who had also been allowed in to this room today turned their noses towards the delicious smell. In anticipation of delicacies to come, they continued to play around, but in a subdued manner, keeping an eye on us. Bubkir lay on the ground and Rbib pulled his legs and tickled the soles of his feet. Always smiling, like his mother Hashouma, Bubkir got up and waddled around in his short shirt, a yellow handkerchief pinned to his chest. He cruised happily from one of the women to another, kissing a hand or a cheek extended towards him. The master's seven-year-old nephew Saleh sat in apparent quiet and dignity; still, his hand slipped stealthily out of his orange *djellaba*, trying to pinch Rbib or pull his hair.

Lalla Zaleha, who sat next to Hafida, stretched and got up; she may have wanted to cross the floor and pick up some small cakes that were on the tea tray by Keltoum. But before she could take a single step, Hafida shot out her leg in a flash and tripped Zaleha, who stumbled and fell at her feet. The others tried to laugh it off as a good-natured prank, but Zaleha did not join them. The co-wife had again tried to make her appear ridiculous.

To my surprise, Zaleha was not the only person in the room who did not join in the laughter. Lalla Keltoum too, her expression unusually hard, seemed to take a disdainful measure of both her co-wives. But immediately, as if afraid of being observed, she cast her eyes down and resumed her impassive expression.

I inspected her in more detail. Her rolled-up sleeves bared her round white arms and rows of golden bracelets. Her finger tips were slender, her oval nails carefully stained pinkish brown with henna. She had planted a petal-like pea-size red dot between her brows. Her full and very light face was surrounded by the yellow fringes of a headcloth which fell to her shoulders. The headcloth itself was of purple silk, as smooth as glass; intentionally, it left part of her forehead and her pitch-black hair uncovered. A thin ribbon at the forehead prevented the kerchief from falling off, and served too as a delicate way of taming the small curls at her temples. A loose flowery taffeta skirt and corsage gave the young Lalla an unambiguously bridal appearance. Was that meticulously clothed and painted lady the humble and unobtrusive Keltoum? What had made her change so?

The spits with meat were served, and we pulled off the succulent bits with fingers. Zaleha deemed the moment ripe for a counter-blow:

'I fail to understand why Lalla Hafida gives Rbib so much to drink,' she said provocatively. 'For every piece of meat, a gulp of water. I don't think it's good for his health. Is it, *tbib*?'

In contrast to her usual demeanour, Zaleha's tone was haughty and condescending. She acted as if her co-wife were not in the room. Hafida listened, and looked sharply at Zaleha. When the unsuspecting *tbib* agreed with Zaleha, Hafida uttered venomously: 'I get it.' She ate a few more mouthfuls and then left the room, saying she had a headache.

Zaleha laughed gaily in her inimitable way:

'Lalla Hafida's health isn't something to boast about. That's because she eats all the time. We domestic wives are like puppies: we are for ever stuffing ourselves. We are not in the habit of eating only at fixed mealtimes like you Europeans do. We always have food on hand — and an appetite.'

She became sombre:

'Lalla Hafida cannot stand me. And when she is furious with me, she sometimes really does get ill.'

She nodded towards the door through which Hafida had gone out:

'Lalla Hafida has three hearts. One is for herself, and that one is generous. The other is for the household, and that one isn't bad either. Her third heart is for me, and that one is wicked.'

Keltoum also left our company without saying a word. She had sat at her tray all the time, her air somehow contrived and stiff. Now she slipped away as if she were in great hurry.

Had I known then what was about to happen, I would have looked into her chamber. I would have seen her stop and listen anxiously: was any member of the household close by? She went stealthily to her couch, knelt beside it and slipped her hand under the mattress. It lighted on the object she was looking for: a *merroud*, the size of a large piece from a chess set. An empty *merroud* with no kohl left in it, some six inches of turned wood varnished yellow. A colourful flower decorated its stouter mid-portion. Keltoum's mother had secretly brought it on the Night of the Spirits. Under no circumstance could anyone else in the house know of the gadget's existence. As she handed it to her daughter, the mother had once again whispered in her daughter's ear these supremely important and potent magic words:

'I tie you down against a hundred women and two women . . .'

Keltoum now briefly closed her fingers round the *merroud* and hurriedly hid it again under her mattress.

KELTOUM

It was already two weeks since the great feast, and the third week had begun when I once again walked to Hadj Kadur's house. To my surprise a totally unknown servant opened the door. She looked at me strangely and suspiciously, unaware of my ties of friendship with the house. Leaving me in the hall, she went to announce my arrival.

The front door had hardly closed behind me when a strange feeling seized me in the darkness of the hall. You cannot explain the indescribable, as this feeling was.

Aunt Yamina soon arrived, dragging her feet. Her rumpled velvet dress and tangled hair suggested that she had been wakened from her siesta. She kissed me in the familiar way and pulled me by the hand into the patio while at the same time showering me with reproaches for having been away for so long.

All the servants were huddled together in the patio: Hashouma, the younger girls, and the kitchen hags. Some fire-chafed sheep's heads, still with their horns, were spread out on the floor tiles. The business at hand was to scrape off the charred layer from the skin. These heads had been freshly bought in the market, as they often were in preparation for feasts, since boiled tongues and brains were highly appreciated.

I approached and bade them Allah's support in their work. In contrast to the servants' usual amiable and even jocular behaviour towards me, I only heard a mumbled response, and their foreheads sank even lower over the sheep's head. Only Hashouma thanked me in the usual manner. When I had been standing for a little while near to the women, I realised that for some reason my presence was an embarrassment to them.

The double door of Lalla Keltoum's chamber behind the labourers' backs was closed, but I found Lalla Hafida and Lalla Zaleha sitting side by side in Zaleha's room. 'War! this means war between us!' Hafida cried out. 'Where have you been so long? Did you forget about us?' The ladies could not shake hands, because their hands were thickly covered with brown henna mush so that they looked more like gingerbread.

So they were busy applying henna. They had reciprocally drawn geometrical designs on their hands with the end of a henna stick, and now they were drying them over a chafing dish. The mush was beginning to crack and peel off, revealing an interesting dark brown 'mitten' design tanned in the skin. Such decorated hands made a good match for the splendour of their festive gowns. Was there a celebration in the offing? My modest inquiry to that effect brought no clarification. They fleetingly looked at each other and smiled enigmatically — that was all.

Lalla Hafida jumped up. Holding her half-dry works of art high up, she called excitedly: 'Come and play the piano!'

Piano? What piano? Confused, I followed Lalla Hafida into her chamber. I could hardly believe my eyes when I saw, facing me, a genuine dark brown upright piano, filling almost the entire end of the room, and leaning clumsily against the wall. And leaning against it, crosswise, was a tall and defiant white European clothes cabinet complete with a mirror. I stared in amazement at these two intruders, trying not to smile at how incongruous they seemed alongside the unobtrusive room furnishing. But perhaps I should have felt an urge to cry, because the comfortable and lovely dinner corner was gone. Modern times had thrust their first wedge into the quiet and attractive Moorish culture of this house.

I had no choice, in this situation, but to look as if I shared Hafida's enthusiasm. My voice said 'Mzian bzef, very good!' while inside I wanted to shout at the cabinet: 'Get out of here!'

At Hafida's behest yet another piece of furniture was hastily brought in: a piano stool. A broken mechanism meant that it could not be raised to its proper height, and therefore the piano player had to grope for the keyboard almost at face level. But it was none the less a European stool, and the hostess pushed it under me with great feelings of pride.

The master-player of course turned out to be Lalla Hafida herself. The piano was not unknown to this former professional musician. She wiped what remained of the henna off her hands and demonstrated a peculiar technique, her left hand scanning the rhythm of an Arab tune while the right hand slid over the keys in rapid cycles.

Aunt Yamina listened in rapture. Zaleha also joined us in measured steps. She was now wearing a muslin *dfina* with golden yellow stripes. Black suede gloves protected her freshly hennaed hands.

The tea tray waited for us in the chamber, and so did Hashouma with her water kettle. But where was Lalla Keltoum, who habitually brewed the tea?

'Has Lalla Keltoum been hennaed, too?' I asked. No one answered. Hafida turned sharply toward Hashouma: 'Go and bring some almonds for madame!' Almonds came, and so did many more dishes. One command followed another. Their eagerness to be good hosts was extraordinary. I then tried again.

'Is Lalla Keltoum in good health?' I asked politely, munching a cake. Again no one replied. I looked about in puzzlement. They avoided my glance. Had Keltoum caught a contagious disease so that she was being kept behind closed doors? But this was impossible: they would have called for the *tbib*.

In which room could she be? The kitchen? Upstairs? And why did they refuse to talk? What was behind it all?

I was urged unceasingly to eat and drink. They even brought out the household's most splendid and rarely used tiny expensive teacups. The women's behaviour was strange. Their hospitality was so excessive that it inevitably gave the impression that they wanted to avoid answering awkward questions by offering food. Were they annoyed that I had mentioned Keltoum's name?

The indescribable feeling that had gripped me in the hall did so again with renewed force. Neither the ladies nor the servants were the same as before. Or was it I who, without knowing it, was not well so that my oversensitive nerves produced figments of imagination?

I was startled by Lalla Zaleha's sudden laughter — short, nervous and without cause. It stopped as suddenly as it began. Aunt Yamina pulled herself up, rushed to the radio set, and rapidly turned its buttons at random. A primeval bellow shook the room. When its volume was brought under control, it became a song by Vahvad, the Eygptian — mostly a refrain 'O ... *dee, o ... dee.*'

'What is it exactly he's singing about?' I asked.

'He is singing about his beloved one,' Aunt Yamina replied. 'He loves her so very, very much . . .' She pressed her crossed fists eagerly against her chest as if her heart threatened to burst.

No, I had to get rid of this strange feeling and persuade myself that the atmosphere in the house was as usual — quiet and secure. So, with deliberation, I asked a third question about Keltoum:

'May I give my greetings to Keltoum?'

A new silence . . . and then everyone began to talk hurriedly as if they had not even heard my question. When I frowned, Aunt Yamina said hesitantly: 'She . . . went . . . out . . .'

Noticing Lalla Hafida's severe glance, Aunt Yamina pulled her head down between her hunched shoulders and slipped out of the room like a child who has been scolded.

Keltoum went out? Where could a harem wife go by herself? They only went to the baths, and then in a group and at night. The only exception was visiting one's mother when she was critically ill. But such a rare happening was nothing to be secretive about, although a servant would certainly be needed as escort. Only as a bad joke could I imagine, suddenly transformed into a European scene, a high-heeled Keltoum going out alone and ambling along the streets, wearing a hat and with a pocket-book dangling from her fingers. It was a grotesque picture — but I was certain now that something had happened in this house in the past two weeks when I had not visited — something to keep deathly quiet about, either because there was to be some domestic feast — or, because of something connected with Keltoum herself.

On my way home I kept pondering over the secretiveness they had shown about Keltoum: I could not get rid of this worrying feeling.

Shortly afterwards, I was glad to run into Rahel in a small street in the heart of the old city. Our conversation soon touched on Hadj Kadur's harem. I told her about the odd impressions I had had on my latest visit there. What I said seemed to unsettle and irritate Rahel. She pretended she was in a hurry and tried to move off, but I seized her arm and did not let go:

'Tell me, Rahel, what has happened in that house? What's the story about Keltoum? You do know about it. I know that you know!'

Her resistance began to weaken under my onslaught, until at last she looked anxiously around us and then determinedly led me into the nearby archway. And there, next to a heap of kitchen waste waiting in a corner for the next round of the city garbage cart; there, standing by a pile of orange and potato peelings, and other scraps with the body of a dead cat thrown on the top — there I learned everything, and I will try to convey the account which Rahel feverishly whispered to me. The telling of it alone seemed to release some of the obsessive pressure of her secret.

TKA' AF

On the evening of the third day of *El-Aid*, the feast after the fast, Rahel went to greet Hadj Kadur, who had just returned from the capital city. The delightful aromas of festive dishes still hung in the air along with people's thoughts during that late evening which had begun in such a carefree way, without so much as a hint of its dramatic outcome.

Rahel took along a cake for the master of the house — a cake with many layers, baked of the finest sifted wheat flour, so fluffy and foamy that it hardly seemed to be made of flour. The Muslim city-dwellers did not make such cakes; only the matrons of the *mellah*, the Jewish quarter, knew how to bake the *beskouit*, as it was called. Through Rahel, Hadj Kadur had already made its acquaintance some time ago — he had laughed at its amazing softness but appreciated its taste, which was enhanced by the alternation of sweet and aromatic layers.

The Jewess had found the women of the house totally exhausted — the ladies no less than the servants. Throughout the day the house had been assailed by groups of well-wishers. They came and went, drawn by their desire to shake the hand of someone who had stood in the presence of the king. By the evening the tea kettles were empty and the sugar cones had dissolved. The supper prepared for a select circle of gentlemen had been a sumptuous one with numerous meat dishes, a heap of couscous, and a *bastila* pie more than half a metre in diameter prepared by Lalla Ftuh.

By the time of Rahel's arrival, all the guests had finally left, and the master of the house had gone out to escort them. The women were enjoying a breather after the battle. Outwardly they were still in a festive mood and feeling satisfied. Lalla Hafida locked up the remaining tea and sugar. Lalla Zaleha, who had prepared several salads, lay down. Aunt Yamina had lost track of how many basketfuls of fresh mint she had cleaned for making tea. Hashouma's hands were swollen with all the kneading of bread dough. Zohra leaned against the wall, waiting for fresh commands, although her feet were sore and stiff from running up and down the stairs, carrying dishes and trays to the guestroom. Ms'ouda was yawning repeatedly. It was a wonder the kitchen hags were still alive amid so much smoke and fumes.

Only Lalla Ftuh felt sufficiently rested to strike up a conversation with Rahel. Yes, she had arrived a full day earlier to prepare the *bastila*. The six pigeons for the filling had to be stewed in saffron early in the proceedings and handfuls of almonds had to be crushed. In the morning thirty boiled eggs and the rest of the necessary items were added to the mix, and then Lalla Ftuh could concentrate on the most important task: baking the sheets of puff pastry. Not everyone was capable of mastering this skill. The sheets had to be baked one by one on a hot iron drum, and come out transparent like tissue paper. Lalla Ftuh had insisted on having not less than a hundred and fifty of them, putting Keltoum to work keeping the charcoal burning at the proper intensity.

Without praising herself, Lalla Ftuh declared the pie a success: a strongly spicy, sweet, and properly salty golden disk decorated with a grid of sugar and cinnamon which was well received by the guests. She only wondered whether the master himself had had time to put a single pinch of it on his own tongue, busy as he was taking care of the guests.

The outer door slammed. The master had returned. He stepped quickly through the patio right into Lalla Hafida's room, dropped his burnous in a single move on the sitting mattress, sat down at the table, and clapped his hands. He was hungry. There always had to be some food in the house for the master. Let them bring swiftly the pieces of meat set aside expressly for him.

He ate quickly and without speaking. The women watched him from the side. When Rahel set the Jewish cake on the table, Hadj Kadur smiled happily and proceeded eagerly to break off pieces of the cake with his fingers. His appetite satisfied, he asked for a knife, cut a suitable piece of the cake, and tendered it on his palm respectfully to Lalla Ftuh. Thereafter, everyone in the room received her share.

Hadj Kadur finished his meal, wished everyone peace in Allah, and walked up to his room, accompanied by Zohra who carried his burnous. It was, of course, time to prepare for the prayer.

Rahel along with the three spouses, Lalla Ftuh, and Aunt Yamina picked at the remains of the meal. There was no denying that the left-overs were the tastiest morsels of well-cooked dishes. After that they were all looking for their couches.

Lalla Ftuh stayed to keep Hafida company. Aunt Yamina lay down at once in Zaleha's chamber, covering herself from head to toe with her *haik*. Rahel was given a blanket and shared the same long mattress, her head beside Aunt Yamina's. Both ladies of the house closed their doors, and so did the servants. The lights were put out. The darkness of the night crept from the sky into the patio.

However, one side of Keltoum's double door was still open, and its white artificial silk curtain was lighted by the lamp in her chamber. Everyone knew why. The lighted doorway was to guide

the master to the couch where he was to spend tonight in case he
had forgotten or mixed up the days. It was Keltoum's turn to
share her bed with the master.

Although they were accustomed to falling asleep immediately,
this time neither Rahel nor Lalla Zaleha was able to do so. The
head of Zaleha's couch faced a low gridded window, almost
touching its coloured panes. Maybe the vivid events of the day
were still stimulating Zaleha's nerves. As for Rahel, her swollen
legs smarted, and she slapped and rubbed them. Zaleha made a few
humorous comments about some of the guests of whom she had
managed to catch a glimpse. She lifted her head and listened, and
so did Rahel: soft quick steps were heard in the patio — going
towards Keltoum's door. It was the master. Keltoum's door was
pulled shut, and all was quiet.

Rahel thought about Zaleha. She knew that Zaleha had long
ago become accustomed to the prevailing situation in the house,
and no longer cared one way or the other. On a few occasions she
had opened her heart to Rahel. Sharing her husband with
Keltoum had been tough in the beginning, but it was nothing
compared to the mental agony caused by Hafida's arrival. Zaleha
had told her about that horrible first night when, picturing her
husband's lustful arms wrapped around the new co-wife, she had
stood the whole long night grasping at her window in
unquenchable rage, her glance never wavering from the closed
door opposite. She clung to the grating, bit her lips and her nails
until they bled, and showered the intruder with death curses.
Only gradually had she been forced by fate to submit.

Now Zaleha showed only happiness at her husband's return
from his journey. She asked Rahel if she was warm and pulled her
blanket over her head. The chamber became silent. The whole
house was asleep. Exhaustion caught up with Rahel and she too
fell asleep.

A shrill scream shattered the silence of the night.

Rahel jerked upright. She did not know whether she had slept
for a short or a long time — what sort of a voice was that? Where
had it come from? Hadn't it come from the direction of

Keltoum's chamber? Zaleha was awake too. And now, as clear as could be, there came another shriek which faded away into a kind of rattle. Icy shivers ran down Rahel's spine. She and Zaleha jumped to their feet and opened the door a little.

By that time Lalla Hafida's door was wide open, and the servants were bunched together at the threshold of their room. All were gaping at Keltoum's chamber with horror all over their faces, and without daring to move a muscle. Hadj Kadur's enraged shouting could be heard. One side of Keltoum's double door burst open, and the master's arm hurled some object — smack! — against the servants' door at the opposite side of the patio.

Hashouma picked it up. It was a small *merroud* made of turned wood, with a red blossom painted on it. In a moment Hafida was beside the servant and had grabbed the object. She recoiled as she looked at it.

'A *tka'af!*' she gasped, immediately understanding the truth.

'*Tka'af!*' The terrible, blood-curdling word travelled from mouth to mouth.

Lalla Hafida ran to the kitchen as if the tiny bottle of kohl were burning her hand, threw the *merroud* on the still glowing charcoals, and heaped them on top of it.

'*Tka'af!*' reverberated through Rahel's skull. *Jehova! Jehova Sabaoth!*

Had Lalla Keltoum really dared? That very young and subdued one? Who had instructed, incited and counselled her? Her mother . . . of course. And now, indeed, she had indulged in that terrible black magic curse, with the help of a *merroud*. What had her purpose been? To make Hadj Kadur impotent, of course — with every woman but herself. This was the crime that every male dreaded more than death. The act that every bridegroom was afraid of, so that at the wedding a witch woman was invited to the feast to undo the curse.

Keltoum had set the *merroud* and the little stick that went with it in a certain position on the carpet, and enticed her husband to step over them. She had then put them in a small bag and folded its opening over, shutting it, while pronouncing the magic words:

'I tie you down against a hundred women and . . .' This was the end of Hadj Kadur's male power. O Jehova of the heavenly hosts, come and help!

Both sides of Lalla Keltoum's door suddenly burst open. The master's arms dragged Keltoum on the threshold and dumped her in the patio where she lay in a crumpled heap. Hadj Kadur's swarthy face was ashen pale. He was sweating from horror and shock.

'Out! Out of my house!' His voice was hoarse with rage. 'Let Shiban get a cart-driver this very moment! Out with her and all her things!'

Lalla Ftuh stepped up to him:

'In the name of gracious and merciful Allah, please say: did you step over it?'

'No . . . I did not step over it . . . my toe hit it . . . touched it, so I got a warning . . .'

Relieved, Lalla Ftuh kissed her own palms in fervent devotion: 'Praised be Allah, the almighty!'

'I suspected it looking at her face,' the master stammered the words out. 'She was sitting on the edge of her couch, and her eyes were wide open. When I went toward her she realised that I had guessed what she was up to, and then she screamed — out of fear. I seized her neck with my hands and she shrieked. I squeezed, but it didn't kill her. . . . Out with her, I say!'

Lalla Ftuh stood self-confidently in front of him:

'In the Prophet's name, listen to me, Hadj. Put your burnous on and go to the *taleb* Ferid — hurry. I know the *taleb* and his house. He has medicine ready to use against this dreadful spell: snake skins and turtle scales. Let him fumigate you at once to remove any possible new danger. The main thing is that he should not be sparing with resins, turpentines and the Persian faeces. Those last things will certainly make you stink to high heaven and make you feel sick, but it will dilute the curse and strengthen your manhood.'

The wise and knowledgeable Lalla Ftuh was already imagining the *taleb* in action and imitated his mysteries in her noseless snuffling voice, raising all five fingers: 'If it's a woman's curse, let it

come to nought. If it's the *djnun*'s malediction, let it be thwarted
. . .' She concluded her advice:

'From the *taleb*'s you will go directly to the baths and wash
yourself. Zohra, fetch the master's burnous.'

Lalla Ftuh's dignified and positive behaviour calmed Hadj
Kadur. His anger subsided, and as he gazed at the prostrate
woman a spark of compassion may have crossed his mind: had not
Keltoum acted out of sheer passionate love towards him? But,
even so, did that mean he had to accept loss of control over his
manly power, he whom Allah had created a male to rule over
females? His recent fright was still vivid in his mind, and resentment was the dominant emotion in his heart as he muttered in a
calmer voice:

'She cannot stay here. Let her return to her mother.'

'This shall be done,' Lalla Ftuh replied firmly. 'She shall go
right away accompanied by Shiban. However, her mattress will be
delivered tomorrow — do the women of the city have to be given
a bone to gnaw at by gossiping in the baths about you and your
household? Under her *haik* no one will recognise her tonight, and
as we take the mattress tomorrow we will say that moths have got
at it and that the couch is being taken for a wash. That's what
we'll do. But be quick now, and may Allah help you.'

As soon as the master had left, Lalla Hafida, her eyes full of
rage, pounced on Keltoum and spat on her:

'You dog! You snake! You wanted to bewitch the master for
yourself alone and force us out. May fever blot you out! May you
vanish from this world, and may you have a candle at your head
and your feet!'

Lalla Zaleha was also shaken and indignant, and with good
reason, but above all else she felt deeply insulted. She shook her
fists at Keltoum:

'May all sorrows hit you!' Lalla Zaleha began to cry.

Lalla Ftuh cut short these outpourings by the co-wives. She
instructed Rahel:

'Go into her chamber and get her *haik*, her face covering and
her slippers. Tie a caftan of the warmer kind into a bundle and
anything else you happen to come across.'

When this was done, she ordered Keltoum to get up and wrapped her and her face into the *haik*. The rest of the women kept away as if afraid to touch her. The dazed Keltoum accepted everything. One of her earrings became detached and fell to the floor. Aunt Yamina at once grabbed it greedily, and would have pocketed it, but Lalla Ftuh's curt order cut her short:

'Give it back.'

At the outer door, where Shiban was waiting, Lalla Ftuh put her hand on Keltoum's shoulder:

'O little daughter, go and face your punishment. In your youthful blindness you allowed yourself to be led astray by your mother — may her days be short! Seek to atone for your grave sin by prayer and fasting. May Allah open a road before you.'

Keltoum and Shiban vanished from sight into the bleary darkness of the new moon, Shiban carrying the bundle and leading the way, and Keltoum reeling and stumbling after him.

Assisted by Hashouma, Lalla Ftuh used the herbs left over from the Night of the Spirits to fumigate Keltoum's room and destroy everything that had harm and magic about it.

Rahel's account was reaching its end:

'The next day Lalla Ftuh and I gathered up Keltoum's belongings. There wasn't much of anything because Keltoum had not brought any room furnishings to the house — all she had were bought by the master. We loaded the wool mattress on the cart and stuck the new red blanket, the pillows, and Keltoum's clothes under it. The cart took them away . . .'

As Rahel spoke, I had a vision of a cart, and distinctly heard the turning of the wheels on the narrow bumpy pavement, just as I had heard the wheels of the neighbour's cart on the 27th of Ramadan, the Night of the Spirits. That time they brought someone; now they were taking someone away . . . Wasn't there suddenly an arrogant and malicious noise mingled with the rattle of the wheels, like a *djinn*'s deep subterranean laughter? Of course, that was merely the iron hoop of the wheel creaking on the gravel . . .

Rahel and I both breathed heavily. I remembered something else:

'Rahel, when Lalla Hafida and Lalla Zaleha hennaed their hands, what festivities were they preparing for? Why wouldn't they say what it was?'

Her expression softened, and she continued in a tender mood:

'Children. Because of the children. Hadj Kadur consented to bring stepchildren into the house. He even seemed happy with the idea, for what sort of house is it without children? Yes, the stout one is quite enterprising, there's no denying that. Through an old woman, she arranged for a daughter for herself and another for Zaleha. They say that boys are harder to get, but mere girls do not cost much at all. The very night of your visit the hag was supposed to bring the children. No outsider could be present. The evil eye . . . you know . . . But now the children have arrived. You and the *tbib* should go without delay and congratulate the new mothers.'

Rahel got ready to leave, smiling with pleasure. After a few steps she halted and said over her shoulder:

'But be sure you do not praise the children, as your custom is. You know this can bring the children bad luck.'

EPILOGUE

What is there to tell about the later lives of the two harem wives, Lalla Hafida and Lalla Zaleha?

Children? They both later had three or four of them. The years passed. New Ramadans came and went. But the deep enmity between the two women was never dissipated. Thus the children, too, grew up as two separate families, and no genuine warmth or trust ever developed between the two camps.

NEVERMORE

(1945)

Sidi Mohammed's brown-spotted coat flashed ahead of me in the souk, through the jostling crowd of *djellabas*. I caught up with him, and we exchanged greetings. How was his wife, Lalla Mouyna?'

'Pretty well,' he said.

Emerging from the souks, we walked together to the corner of the Djemaa el-Fna square, where our paths would separate. He would turn back to his home in the old Arab city, and I would take the bus right there at the small bus-station to the European city outside the wall. However, he did not accept my hand as I offered it to say good-bye. Instead he said: 'I want to talk with you.'

He glanced at the café bordering the square, but then turned towards the bus-station: 'Let's go there, under the trees.'

With a lordly gesture of his hand, he shooed away a Berber youth who was slumbering on a bench. We sat down. He took a cigarette packet from his pocket, apologising for smoking in my presence. Lighting the cigarette, he inhaled a couple of times, then announced brusquely: 'I have got a divorce from Lalla Mouyna.'

I almost burst out laughing. What kind of a joke was this? Hadn't I visited them with the *tbib* only this last Saturday, as we often did? Everything had seemed fine, and how could it be otherwise? One would have been hard put to find another couple like them. They were without children but had lived together for more than a dozen years, were used to each other and fond of each other. Sidi Mohammed had never felt the least urge to adorn his home with another wife in addition to the light-skinned, chubby Lalla Mouyna.

It was true that twice during their long cohabitation quarrels had exploded. People are not made of stone, after all. On both occasions Sidi Mohammed had rushed to the *cadi* and had his 'marriage card' torn up. There was nothing out of the ordinary or

166

earthshaking about that. Divorces occurred in nearly every marriage. The marriage contract was declared void, only to be reinstated a short while later at the husband's request. The last time this particular couple had had such a reconciliation, and renewed their 'marriage papers', Sidi Mohammed had asked the *tbib* to bring Lalla Mouyna home in his car — she had spent the days of separation at her mother's. The *tbib* gladly obliged, and we had a merry celebration of the new marriage of the two happy people with a sumptuous roast turkey and various other festive dishes.

What was the reason this time? Surely another pointless quarrel. I studied Sidi Mohammed out of the corner of my eye. He was smoking, looking up at the tops of the trees. Never mind the reasons, I mused. Whatever it was, the cure is the same as before. The *cadi*'s writ will join them together again for the third time.

The third time . . . An awful fright seized me. Couples who divorced for three times were not allowed to marry each other again — that was the law. Sidi Mohammed and Lalla Mouyna no longer entitled to remarry! I was stunned. I could imagine Lalla Mouyna, indignant and miserable at her mother's house, having irretrievably lost her husband and her home.

'How miserable Lalla Mouyna must be . . .' I sighed.

Sidi Mohammed nodded assent: 'Indeed. She is crying.'

'Did you go and see her?'

'This is prohibited, since we are no longer husband and wife.'

'Tell me at least, why did you again go to the *cadi*?'

Sidi Mohammed dropped his half-smoked cigarette, and stamped on it. 'That happened the very evening you dined with us. You remember seeing two of my best friends, whom I also invited? For their enjoyment I had asked three of the town's most famous *chikhas* to come and dance. Only through my special connections was I able to get them, and the price was steep. Surely you remember?'

Of course I did. Never before had I encountered such noble *hetairai*. They were highly elegant in their high-collared long-sleeved caftans. They differed from common *chikhas* by their refined behaviour and more sophisticated conversational style.

They even spoke passable French. One of them was particularly noticeable for her youth, beauty and modesty. Together we ate the dinner so skilfully prepared by Lalla Mouyna, who did not take part in the feast herself. It would have been shameful for her to show herself to other men, especially in the presence of *chikkas*. After the meal the host asked them to dance, and the 'Moroccan geishas' readily agreed. Their feet moved evenly, while their bodies kept a graceful pose.

We left soon after, expressing our thanks. In the patio we ran into Lalla Mouyna, who knowingly whispered in my ear:

'Earlier I cut a hole in the window curtain, so I could see from the patio all that you were doing in the chamber.' We laughed, leaving the house behind us in peace and happiness.

Sidi Mohammed went on with his confession: 'Of course, the party took a different turn after your departure. The *chikhas* are not paid just to engage in graceful dancing. As soon as you left they began to show their true professional skills. They did belly-dances and hugged and embraced us. . . . The youngest *chikha* sat on my knee. There's no need to recall all that. . . . As she left the house, the younger *chikha* enticed me to come along, and pulled me by the hand. As we approached the outer door, Lalla Mouyna suddenly came out behind me with a slipper in her hand — and bang! she hit the *chikha* on the head. The *chikha* started screaming. There was such a hue and cry. My friends taunted me: ''You aren't a man if you continue to keep such a wife in your house!'' I was hopping mad. I could have strangled Lalla Mouyna for such an insult to my honour as the master of the house. In the morning I rushed straight to the *cadi* and let him tear up my marriage contract! Then I announced the divorce to my wife, and she moved to her mother's the very same day.'

So this was the outcome of our feast! Under other circumstances it would have been funny — the very idea of Lalla Mouyna whacking a husband-seducing *chikha* with a slipper! Now, however, the way matters had turned out was sad indeed.

'What do you plan to do now?' I asked lamely. His response was loud and clear: 'I'll get married again.'

I stared at him dumbfounded, not expecting that he would give

such a reply at this early stage. With Lalla Mouyna hardly out of
the house, you get another woman in her place! Was that the true
nature of our dear friend Sidi Mohammed? For more than ten
years he had managed to appear as a high-minded man. Only now
were we seeing him in his true colours!

'Aren't you even sorry for poor Lalla Mouyna?' I stammered.

'Of course I am. She must marry without delay.'

'How can you be sure that she is in such a hurry to marry a
stranger?' Female resentment gave my question a derisive note.

'Of course she is. I have even picked a husband for her myself.
One of my friends. He already has a wife, but that doesn't
matter.'

I started feeling strange. After such a long stay in Morocco, was
I still unable to catch on and make sense of these people? Was I not
even capable of knowing my own friends? I felt deeply disturbed,
and wearily leaned my head against the back of the bench. Beside
me, Sidi Mohammed was perking up. Shaking his shoulders as if
to brush off all annoyance, he gaily remarked:

'Presumably the *tbib* will agree to bring my bride home in his
car, as he did the last time? You might make the request in my
name?'

That was too much. Eyes flashing, I snapped: 'And how would
we happen to know who your new bride is, what her name is
and where she lives!'

Sidi Mohammed stared at me in wonderment for quite a while.
Then slowly a broad grin started to form on his lips, but in the end
it did not materialise. His face became serious again, and he put his
hand on my shoulder:

'My apologies,' he said soothingly. 'My apologies. I did not
know that you did not know. To wit, the marriage law includes
one further stipulation. A couple three times divorced can rejoin
again, if the woman has meanwhile been married to another man.
My friend serves as this make-believe other man. He and his wife
want to help us.'

Only now did Sidi Mohammed laugh openly: 'Naturally I
would only marry my little wife Lalla Mouyna!'

FATHERLY LOVE
(1955)

Selim sat cross-legged on the mat outside his door, right across from the darkening pomegranate trees. He was conferring with his own conscience.

In the morning, as he ploughed the master's field, he had not yet felt any need for such deliberation. Everything was clear in his head, and his work went smoothly — for once, the bigger of the two oxen was not pushing its partner with its horns. It was true that just before noon Driss had once again messed things up. Among the four young men who worked under him, Driss was the sloppy one. Today he had brought a cartload of reeds to the farmhouse and dumped the whole lot in the middle of the road.

But the person who had really disturbed Selim's soul was the master himself — that *tbib*, the doctor. He had driven out from the city to his farm in the afternoon to have a talk with Selim.

Nervously, Selim lifted his stork's nest of a turban, passing his hand over the shining clean-shaven crown of his head. Yes, none other but the *tbib*! The physician admittedly knew this country's way of life fairly well, and he was not a bad man, but he surely was a Christian. This was the way Allah had created him, in His wisdom — praised be His name! The *tbib* was not lacking in worldly wisdom, but is that all a man needs?

Every time the well-known sound of the doctor's klaxon was heard at the gate, everyone at the farm started running around. 'Selim! Where is Selim?' the *tbib* would call out, with one leg still inside the car. Then he would proceed in long strides from place to place, asking questions and giving orders. Here he would burst out laughing, next he would fulminate. He would stick a plaster on a labourer's grazed knee, and sometimes even thrust a needle into a donkey's buttock. In no time, all contentious issues would be settled, he would turn his car round and drive off. But none the less, he remained a Nasrani, a Christian. That was why he had given Selim those bizarre commands today.

170

The loud cackle of chickens interrupted Selim's line of thought. Of course, they had a squabble to get themselves better roosting places every evening. The pomegranate tree was full of their dark shapes. For a while they would seem to quieten down and go to sleep, and then one of them would start cackling again, and stir up a general uproar.

From the kitchen door opening to his left, the glow of a fire began to shine on the bushes. Rays of light also filtered through the kitchen wall of woven reeds. Framed in the low entrance Selim could see in the light of the flame his wife's bare arm moving in circles over a round wooden bowl that stood on the ground. She was rubbing butter with her palms into the steamed granules of couscous.

The buzz of children's voices in the kitchen sometimes grew into shrieks, which were rapidly hushed. Now Tibaria stepped out, swinging an empty bucket in her hand. Her bare heels flashing, she swept quickly past her father, as if she were afraid of him, or ashamed of something.

His head askew and his neck craned, Selim kept peering after her, as if he was seeing his daughter for the first time. He had not changed his position when the girl returned with water, her figure still like that of a child. Her body tilted under the weight of water, and her thin arm was taut like a steel cable. Her legs were thin too — Selim watched as they trudged quickly, yet stiffly. The printed cotton shawl over her head was hung down to her waist — and now the girl had even pulled it up to her eyes!

What the *tbib* had said that afternoon came back to Selim like a thunderbolt. Brusquely, without any forewarning, the boss had said to him:

'Listen, Selim, there's talk among the women that your family is preparing for a wedding. I just wanted to know whose wedding it could be, since Tibaria is still a child. Why are you pushing such a little girl into marriage? How old is she, anyway? Ten? Twelve? Have you thought of the fact that girls must not marry before they reach womanhood? Tell me, has she started having periods yet?'

Selim felt as if he had fallen from the clouds. He stared at the boss, unable to utter a single word. The question was shockingly indecent. What business had the *tbib* with such a female matter? Only when the physician repeated the inquiry was he able to reply: 'I don't know' — and that was the plain truth.

'If so, go at once, and ask your wife. Go right away, go, go! Bring me the answer. I'll wait.'

Selim inched toward his quarters with the utmost reluctance. How could he ask Lalla R'kia about such a thing? He was a man. He peered over his shoulder. The doctor stood his ground, waiting.

It took quite a while before he could make his wife understand what he was trying to say, and he could understand her. He returned to the *tbib*, and blurted out:

'She hasn't.'

'Well, you see: she's still a child. What's the hurry about getting her a husband? Give the child time to become an adult. You've got to wait. Such is Allah's command.'

That was exactly what the physician had said: it was Allah's command! What does a Christian, who does not know a single *sura* of the Koran, know of Allah's commands? Even on his own deathbed he could not seek salvation by intoning the credo. Allah? Yes, it was precisely Allah who had helped Selim to find a son-in-law with a home of his own, a clean room and food on the table. And had not Allah himself entered Tibaria's wedding date into the book of her fate?

It was Allah too who had instilled in Selim's heart that deep paternal love, which commanded him to give his daughter away to a strange household at such an early age. This was like giving away a kitten. Loving was the hand who tore it away from the mother's breast at such a tender age. The little one would whimper around for a couple of days — and then she would get used to the new surroundings. It was heartless, in contrast, to give away a larger kitten — such a one would cry and struggle for weeks, often running away and courting death. Would Selim be so heartless as to subject Tibaria to such torture? Certainly the child was weeping at the moment and feeling embarrassed to face her father, but soon she would be more cheerful than ever. A young person's liver is still soft, so a child adjusts easily. She would resign herself to the new surroundings and to being bossed by her mother-in-law. And she would turn out more obedient and submissive to her husband.

It was true that Lalla R'kia was sighing and weeping secretly along with her daughter. That was how women were. Yet she herself had gone through the same experience. She was no older at the time of her wedding than Tibaria was now, nor had she known Selim beforehand — but was she unhappy? Had Selim ever left his family without food? He had not even taken an additional wife into the household. But now Lalla R'kia was turning on the waterworks and saying: 'Mekki will start out as an utter stranger to Tibaria.' What did it matter in mating, whether the partner's face was familiar or not? A woman's line of reasoning was inconsistent, anyway: at first they cried, and later they would desperately try to hold on to their husbands. And you may think that you are giving a mere child in marriage, but lo and behold, soon the child will be nursing a child herself!

Once again, Selim's train of thought was disturbed — this time by an approaching glare of light. As if conjured up by his thoughts of her, Lalla R'kia was coming out of the kitchen, carrying a storm lantern in one hand and a tray of glasses in the other. Her caftan train was pulled up and stuck into her waistband. The lantern cast a pale pencil of rays on her wide baggy breeches, which left the legs bare half way up her shins. With a quiet smile, Lalla R'kia gave the evening greeting, and set the lantern before Selim and the tea tray at one side.

Selim took a gulp of hot mint tea, then another. It was strange — not even the tea tasted right this evening. The *tbib*'s words had robbed him of that pleasure too. Hadn't the physician gone on and told him about a bride who was too young, and whose wedding night had ended in a mishap? But what concern was that story to Selim? The physician had heedlessly continued with his account, as if cutting a notch in Selim's ear with a knife blade — how he, the *tbib*, had tried to help the girl when she was weak from bleeding, in the middle of the night, by candlelight. What did a strange girl matter to Selim? That was the fate Allah had assigned to that particular girl: it did not concern others. But

above all: would the *tbib*, please, not mention the name of the Evil
One, especially in such a loud voice, and right before Tibaria's
nuptials too! The Evil One, the Fiend — may Allah shield us
from him! — was always lurking around, so he would hear when
his name was pronounced, and then attack.

Even when the boss had begun the story, Selim was on his
guard. Very stealthily, he had slipped his hand into his shirt collar
and seized the amulet about his neck. But when it looked as if the
master was not going to desist, Selim became scared. Under no
circumstances should he continue listening. The Evil One, Satan,
could strike at any moment. Selim had fixed his gaze on the toes of
his slippers, mentally repeating the formula to keep the Evil One
at bay:

'In Allah do I seek refuge against the Devil, whom I'll stone to
death! In Allah do I seek refuge against the Devil, whom I'll stone
. . .'

That was as far as he had got when the physician's heavy hand
fell on his shoulder.

'And there's something else, Selim, that you should be concerned about: Mekki himself. He's a fine man, no doubt about it.
He has grown up in your own village and, as his foreman, you can
see what a hard worker he is — who could object to such a son-in-
law? But are you aware that he has a bad disease?'

Selim had breathed relief. At last the conversation was turning
to a more innocuous and pleasant topic. Of course Selim knew. All
workers on the farm knew. They all had seen the pained grimace
on Mekki's face when he went behind a bush to pass water. Why
should Mekki try to hide his ailment: had it not been given to him
by Allah? So Selim replied calmly:

'I know about it.'

'You do? But you must also realise that Mekki received this
disease from women. After all, he's of mature years, over thirty
already, and he surely has not made do without women. And you
also understand that there are many sorts of women. Some are
smooth and fresh on the surface, like an apple, but rotten inside.
That is how Mekki got his disease, and that is how he can also
transmit it to his wife. Do you realise? Your daughter could get

the disease if she marries right now, and then she would be childless.'

Selim could relieve the doctor's worries with a smile:

'Mekki says he is now cured.'

Holy heavens! A wasp seemed to have stung the physician. Eyes flashing, he exploded:

'So what if Mekki did say so? What does Mekki know? I am the one who knows! Only the physician knows, and issues a certificate, when someone is cured. Did those few grains that I gave Mekki to take cure him? Didn't I say: take a week off work, stay with your relatives in the city, and visit me daily for injections. Did he show up? No, he did not! It is your duty now to ask him for a physician's certificate. Tell Mekki: you will not get my daughter unless you can bring me a paper from the *tbib*.'

Those new benighted demands really had Selim flabbergasted. He began to be seized with desperation and to lose his patience. At first he had stood there, carefully shifting his weight from one leg to the other, but at last, to end the intolerable conversation he had shouted '*ouakha!*' (all right) at the *tbib* and fled. The devil, the *shitan* himself, had got hold of the boss today. He had come and, through the mouth of the Nazarene, tried to tempt Selim away from the way of righteousness. Was he, Selim, a man respected throughout the whole village, supposed to make a public fool of himself by postponing the date agreed upon for the wedding? He had even accepted the bride's money from the bridegroom. Was he now to tell Mekki to wait?

Such an indecent proposal could arise only in the mind of someone of a different faith, who had no understanding of the Muslim sense of honour. And for no good reason at all — just because of a disease! Always this Christian apprehension in the face of life, this exaggeration and obfuscation of simple issues! However long those Nazarenes might live, Allah himself did not want them to understand that everything was in the hands of Allah, not of men. It was Allah who bestowed disease, and Allah alone who could remove it, with doctoring and medicines or without. Allah had rid Mekki of his ailment — praise the Almighty! — and Mekki himself was in the best position to know and feel it in his body. But if some germs of the disease still happened to linger in him, then it would be in the hands of Allah alone whether Selim's daughter would contract it or not. If her fate should be to catch the disease, then no power could prevent it — not physicians or their prescriptions. However, it would not have been proper to say all that to the boss. And, anyway, the effort would have been wasted.

The tea in Selim's glass was cold now. His fingers could feel the coolness of the glass. Yet he did not put it back on the tray. He still had to ponder the broad issue. Had he done something wrong? Something against Allah's will? Was he lacking in love for his daughter?

He presumed not. He had behaved in a way that was predetermined by Allah. No word had fallen from his mouth, his feet had not taken a single step without Allah's consent. Laud and praise to Allah for having Selim born a Muslim!

As he placed the glass on the tray, Selim found himself unexpectedly feeling sorry for the *tbib*. The Christian was deprived of true faith and knowledge of Allah's commands. As deprived as a cat huddling in the ashes beside the hearth. Like a cat? Now he was getting it wrong himself. The cat does pray. Whenever it purrs, it prays.

But the Christian toils away at his life without true faith. He is always in a hurry without any reason or cause. On Doomsday the Prophet will not intercede on his behalf: no gardens in Paradise will be set aside for him.

THE FIRST ADDITIONAL WIFE

(1965)

The visitors' room of the *amin* (tax inspector) was a comfortable place. An airy, gypsum-plastered hall, porcelain wall panels, and a single long couch encircling the whole room with plenty of cushions on it so that one could lean against the wall. Among the eight matrons who had come to see the hostess, I was the only foreigner. It was cosy and convivial. The conversation flowed easily and at a slow pace. None of the local ladies had even sat on a school bench — this was left for their children — but they all came equipped with a fair knowledge of the Koran and religious history, and their reserves of life experience were considerable.

Suddenly and unexpectedly the talk took a sombre turn, most likely caused by my own imprudence and naiveté, although the lateness of the afternoon may also have had something to do with it. The time was six o'clock. The festive and heavy eating had gone on for four hours, with plenty of sugarsweet mint tea. Sitting motionless on the same spot had made us somewhat weary, instilling the melancholy thought of returning home to the daily humdrum.

How did this sharp change of mood invade our happy conversation? I was talking with the young and beautiful Lalla Malika, jokingly agreeing that she would come and be an additional wife for my husband. She stood up, laughing. Then she picked up the long train of her caftan, stepped barefoot over the carpet, put on her heelless slippers, and went out to the patio. Meanwhile, my eyes met those of Lalla Fatima, wife of the landowner Sidi Mohammed, who sat opposite to me, her back somehow rigid. She motioned me to come over, and as I sat beside her, she earnestly turned her rather colourless face toward me. Tiny tattoos decorated her forehead and chin: she came from the mountains. Her voice was crackling and manlike:

'It is easy for you to joke about things you don't have to worry about. You are safe in the knowledge that your husband will not

177

take an additional wife into the house. The Prophet — Allah's blessing be with him! — allows our men to marry up to four wives. If you were one of us, and I happened to be your husband's first wife, you would not be laughing.' Lalla Fatima's kohl-lined eyes were glum. Suddenly she clasped my hand in a tight squeeze and went on.

Listen! and tell me whether you would have laughed if you had been in my place. I already had two children, but I was still very young. One evening, as often happened, my husband was to have visitors. Along with the servants, I was rushing to get the dinner prepared, and breast-feeding at the same time, when a servant maid abruptly hurried into the kitchen. Alarmed, she whispered into my ear:

'The master just came into the front porch in the company of three women!'

'Dancers?' I asked.

'Definitely not,' the girl explained. 'They have a man with a pushcart at the door, and they are getting ready to lift a bridal chest into the vestibule. At any rate, it's a purple velvet-covered box decorated with gilded studs all over.'

My soul was confounded. Pulling the feeding baby off my breast, I jumped up. What was the maid jabbering about? What bridal chest? All at once I shook with anguish as never before in my life. As if I were paralysed, I slowly walked across the kitchen patio, opened the door leading to the main patio, and crossed that. As I came into the main room, I saw her.

She was facing our large mirror. Having rid herself of the *haik*, she was adjusting the folds of her caftan. Her hair was full of white velvet flowers, and the wide belt at her waist was pure gold. Noticing my image in the mirror, she turned and asked: 'What's your name, servant?'

My body stopped shaking. I looked straight at her, at her painted face, and replied:

'Who are you, a stranger in these quarters? As for me, I am the lady of the house. I have borne two sons to my husband Sidi Mohammed.'

At once that young woman gave a shriek, and I noticed two older women who immediately got up from the sitting mattress and approached me.

'What kind of a lie is that?' one of them snapped. 'Sidi Mohammed was said to have no real wife, merely servant girls!'

'I am his legal wife!' I loudly reasserted. At the same moment I sensed a need to return to the kitchen. A crushing feebleness below the chest turned my knees shaky. I had to seek support from the patio wall, hardly able to put one foot in front of the other. . . .

Lalla Fatima kept silent for a long time, unconsciously kneading my hand until it hurt. Then her mouth formed itself into a sardonic sneer:

'You see, those dishes I had run myself off my feet to cook that evening — they were for my own husband's wedding feast. . . .'

Once more she lingered, glancing into the void, before continuing in an undertone, as if speaking to herself:

'How I hated that woman — like poison. And I wouldn't hide my feelings when she was around. One day she started to moan, and complain of terrible pains. Sidi Mohammed grabbed me by the shoulders, with anger in his eyes: "Confess! What poison did you put in her food?" By evening a physician was called in. He inspected the woman and gave her an injection. She kept moaning and writhing. The doctor observed her for a while, then exclaimed: "I have injected you with a drug, which immediately removes a person's pain, yet you continue to writhe. You were never in any pain, you are just shamming!" The physician walked out, laughing. The next day that woman had vanished from our household. She was my first co-wife. Oh, later I saw a whole succession of them. Right now there are two quite young ones in our house. . . .'

The other women had listened to Lalla Fatima unburdening herself without interrupting. After a rather depressing pause, the hostess turned to the still youngish spouse of the master-builder, and spoke in her customary unraised voice:

'Lalla Zubida, how are things going with the servants? With Yamina?'

Lalla Zubida had a white face, and her hair was parted straight down the middle. She shifted herself awkwardly and smoothed out the caftan on her knees before finally answering:

'Why call her a servant any longer? She is a lady now . . . and with every day that passes she gets more uppity.'

She looked at Lalla Fatima, as if talking to her alone:

'In my case it did not happen that suddenly at all. . . .'

She kept on gulping, before words came, first in a stutter, then ever more fluently.

Two months ago . . . no, three . . . I began noticing that my husband was casting his eyes towards Yamina. . . . The girl had to be near him and serve him all the time, and when he thought I was not around, he would smile at her, put his hand on her shoulder, or caress her arm. In my company he became more and more grumpy, sitting with downcast eyes. But she only had to appear, and he would look up and follow every move she made. Yamina was soon the only maid who was ordered to serve in his office, which has to open directly on the vestibule because men come there on business — for that reason I could not set foot in there. All the time the girl had to make tea for him, or be present with a tray in anticipation of a visit by business acquaintances.

One day when my husband was alone there, he again called for the girl. I watched the clock and noted that she stayed with him for three whole hours, and yet there was no work to be done. It was now obvious that my husband was lusting after that girl.

Once, returning from a name-giving ceremony at my cousin's, I went to serve food to my husband. He declined my offer almost angrily.

'I don't want any,' he exclaimed.

Among the other delicacies, I had a watermelon, the first one that summer.

'Don't you even want some watermelon?'

'All right, give me some.' He picked among the pieces of melon, put one in his mouth almost reluctantly, and turned towards the door, waiting for Yamina to appear. I plucked up my courage, and asked:

'Allah is supreme! Tell me whether you are craving for Yamina?'

'Yes,' he replied.

'Do you plan to wed her?'

'Yes,' he replied again.

'When?'

He brushed it aside with a gesture of his hand: 'When it's Allah's will.' He rose and left the room.

That was Monday. On Thursday morning he ordered his mother to take the girl to the baths and prepare her for the wedding. As mistress of the household, it was my duty to make the arrangements for the trip to the public baths and to lead the ceremony. I invited aunts, neighbours and servants. We washed that girl, rubbed her with henna, and brought her home, uttering the high-pitched *yu-yus* appropriate to a wedding night.

Then I took refuge with a neighbour. I did not sleep all night. Since the day I dropped out from my mother's womb, I had never cried so dreadfully. If the doctor extracted my heart from my bosom, he would find it shrivelled hard and black like a lump of coal.

The next morning I went home. My husband told me:

'For the feast today, put one of your best caftans on her.' I gave her several. . . .

Silence filled the room again.

At the far end Lalla Moulati, whose husband was in the army, had been lying on her back. A pretty woman, she had no children. She raised herself on her elbows:

'And which of us hasn't gone through the same thing? At first you think that if anything like it ever happens to you, you will either throw yourself into the well or smash your head against a wall. Yet it happens, and you just carry on with the extra wife in the house, although your liver cries out within you, and although,' here her tone became derisive, 'from now on your husband has four eyes — two in front and two behind.'

She suddenly heaved herself up into a sitting position, and lifted both hands, fingers spread wide:

'A man's lust for another woman is like a terrible dust-storm. There is nothing you can do to prevent it, and it just rolls over you.'

Lalla Moulati dropped again on her back, fixing her glance on the cedarwood ceiling high above us. In the quiet of the room, one could then hear the soothing and slightly bewildered words of the elderly Lalla Mina:

'But after all, the master is the cock of the walk!' She looked at the women around her and continued: 'It must be that Allah himself in his wisdom has instilled desire in the body of the man.' Having uttered the name of God, she imploringly kissed both her palms.

Lalla Moulati turned on her side. Her toes adjusted the lamé caftan on her legs. She was already smiling again, and said in a tone of approval: 'My woman neighbour said to me: Don't be silly, don't eat your heart out because of an additional wife. Life is too short for worrying. Five or ten years, maybe a few more, and that's the end of it. Anger is like a vulture: you release it towards another person, but it swings round in full flight, and comes back to peck out your own eyes and liver. Better get some hot coals, pour water on them, and drink it. See then how your peace of mind returns!'

Was it the effect of the neighbour's recipe, or the steaming coffee pot brought in by a servant? Anyway, the mood brightened up at once.

AN EX-CHRISTIAN'S SICK VISIT

(1960)

Custom required that all friends and acquaintances should keep visiting Lalla Fatna during her illness. Her relatives made it a daily practice to come themselves or send a servant to inquire about her condition. So the visitors came and went in droves until the day when Sidi Ali's European wife came to see the sick woman.

Lalla Fatna had been to the baths and looked tired and pale as she sat cross-legged on the high woollen mattress at one end of the narrow, elongated room. She wore her white street *djellaba*, and a white blanket was spread across her lap. Her head was wrapped in a snow-white kerchief tightened with a ribbon tied round her forehead.

Two women visitors crouched on a lower mattress placed at her feet. One of them looked heavy and coarse in her *haik*, and the other, dark-skinned and earnest, looked like a servant.

At the opposite end of the room Lalla Fatima, Lalla Fatna's daughter-in-law, sat on the carpet and offered the visitors tea from a tray in front of her. Just as she was lifting the teapot high and directing the mint- and honey-scented flow into the glasses, Madame Eveline — now renamed Lalla Halima — stepped over the threshold and offered her greetings.

The avid glances of the other visitors bored into the European. They followed her every gesture, as she stepped towards the sick one and kissed her, and hung on every word she uttered. They also scrutinised her as she sat down on the mattress and stretched her feet, with their European shoes, far out on the carpet.

'Everything stems from Allah. That goes for sickness too. We are in the hands of God,' the stouter woman drawled.

'Yes, indeed, we are in the hands of God,' Eveline confirmed, meanwhile contemplating Lalla Fatna's lovely face, which was now so emaciated. What a graphic and painful reminder it was of how soon beauty and wellbeing and even terrestrial existence could so quickly fade away. As the stranger's eyes surveyed her,

183

Eveline saw a taunting smile, almost a sneer, form on the woman's lips, which she did not even attempt to hide. She seemed to fling her sentiments right in Eveline's face. Eveline flared up.

Was she always to remain everywhere and in everyone's eyes an unbeliever, that basest and most despised of all human beings? Would she never come to be treated as a member of this community? Would her conversion never be seen as she saw it? Faith in God could rise to great heights in her, but no one would believe that or care about it. For the people of this country faith consisted not only of spiritual devotion but also of all the manifestations of practical daily life. Everything was subject to prescription: food, clothes, habits, behaviour, relationships, conversation, attitudes. It was not only a religion but a way of life demanded by a civilisation that had developed almost with its own momentum. It governed one's life from morning till evening and from evening till morning. Whoever was different from the norm, whoever did not follow those stagnant forms, prohibitions and commands that dated from centuries gone by — that person was not a true believer.

Eveline was different from her environment. That fact was never forgiven. Today for the first time she felt the need for a counter-attack.

'God is the same for Christians, Muslims and Jews — given that there is not more than one God. What is there to laugh about?' she burst out aggressively.

These words swept the sneer off the stout woman's lips, but a glowering scowl now took its place. What Eveline had said had not improved the woman's opinion of her — the European sensed it acutely.

When the other visitors left soon after the little *contretemps*, Lalla Fatna, with her lean fingers, clasped Eveline's hand in a soothing gesture as if trying to make amends for the injustice which had occurred inside her abode. She groped for words to assuage hurt feelings:

'You see . . . among the Muslims, the younger ones. . . . there are some who no longer follow the right path. Of course, this has also been willed by Allah. They eat pork, they no longer fast properly, and they drink liquor and beer. Yet they are Muslims and remain so. But among the Christians one encounters some who . . . some who . . .' Lalla Fatna stumbled in embarrassment and agitation, and went on in a whisper: '. . . some who actually say . . . there is no God! They do. . . . And then you simply do not know whether you are still dealing with human beings or with vicious *afarits*.'

Lalla Fatna squeezed Eveline's hand as if asking forgiveness for daring to talk like that about Christians to a former Christian. Then she went on more philosophically:

'What is human life? It's like a two-doored chamber. See, one enters from one side and goes out through the other. It's over. It's gone. What can we do about it? Is there any personal merit in being able to hear or being able to see written letters, with glasses or without? God is the one who gives everything. God gives illness and health. Why should we be afraid of disease? When pain keeps me awake at night, I am still not afraid. Life is there so that one can die. Will I die of my present illness? Yes, if Allah has entered it in His book. And if I do not die of this disease, I will of the next one or the one after next. I am at peace. I do take medicine, but Allah will manifest His intentions on whether I shall recover or not.'

More visitors entered — an old Jewess in rags and a servant from some relatives' household. They stayed only a very short time. One lowered oneself in front of the sick one and kissed Lalla Fatna's hand, while the other said, as if reciting a poem, who sent greetings and who was in good health back home. They wished Lalla a quick recovery, got up and quickly left. Why waste words? They would hear soon enough how the sick one fared. The important thing was that they kept her in mind and came to let her see it.

THE GROOM'S VERSION
(1965)

It must have been predetermined by fate that my wedding was to turn out differently from my plans and expectations.

When Silvia and I were both still students in Paris, I had repeatedly tried to relieve her of her worries:

'Dearest Silvia, light of my eyes! You'll never regret coming with me to Morocco. The land of my forefathers has captivated you even through pictures and the descriptions you have read. Just wait: as soon as you set foot on its soil and get to know the people you will be possessed by a warm feeling of being at home.'

Somewhat later I was able to announce to her with delight:

'My mother and uncle have started preparations for our wedding. I have requested that you as the bride will receive all the honours and attention that our centuries-long tradition can offer, even today. You will be enthroned like a queen. My queen! You will shine in silk and brocade, and your beauty will stun the wedding guests.'

I kissed Silvia's corn-coloured hair and her palms, passionately but also with due respect.

I did not mention the wedding expenses. Since my father's death our family's income was no longer anything to boast about. A ditty that was quite well known in my homeland came into my mind, and echoed unpleasantly:

> The Jew's money melts away in religious rites,
> The Christian's money in betting on horses,
> The Muslim's bag is emptied for wedding expenses.

For me there was a grain of truth in those ironic words. At least one of our three houses had to be sold off to go towards the cost of the wedding feast. Mohammed, the highly schooled son of an honourable citizen of Marrakech, is getting married! This fact is going to reverberate throughout the city and will inevitably generate obligations towards a couple of hundred male guests and, separately, towards an equal number of female ones. But then, every official agency in my homeland is yearning to hire a young man with a European education like me, and so the debts can gradually be paid off.

Silvia and I did not have much discussion about religion. Youth from many corners of the world had all come together in Paris, and our belonging to different religions did not hinder us from becoming friends. Silvia had grown up in a northern Protestant country, and I in a southern Islamic one. Did that have to affect our love? Once we arrived in Morocco, Silvia would naturally join me in fulfilling the Islamic religious requirements of our society, and I for my part would not forbid her to attend her own church, it she wished to do so.

As the ship left Marseilles, Silvia was vivacious and cheerful. It was August, and the sky was cloudless. The next day, the sun pinched my skin in a familiar way, and on the third day we arrived in Casablanca. My uncle was there to meet us, and I almost didn't recognise him. I was used to seeing him in a fluffy floor-length national costume, and his European suit was a complete novelty to me. It made him thinner and much younger. After we had embraced and kissed each other, I introduced Silvia. My uncle's sense of decorum only allowed him to cast the most fleeting glance at my bride, but something in his expression as he accepted the handshake she offered him convinced me that he liked her.

The same sense of propriety made us avoid chance encounters with acquaintances and start for Marrakech without delay. My uncle did the driving: in our country the groom usually does not drive his bride home, and why give rise to needless gossip?

Given my uncle's limited command of French, our conversation soon shifted to Arabic. As we talked, my glance hovered delightedly over the stubble fields of the bleached plain where the windowless box-like buildings floated like white ships on the ocean.

Coming back to these wide spaces made my chest expand. The view was no longer blocked by factory chimneys or even by trees. The further we drove inland, the more the land was impregnated by the August heat. Where grain had grown lush during the winter, there were now rusty expanses and only a few isolated animals were visible on the horizon, grazing. Although the landscape was bare and dry, it was full of serenity.

The heat was affecting Silvia in the back seat. She leaned forward, face flushed. She had kept silent all this time, unable to share in our conversation beyond saying 'all right, thank you' each time we asked over our shoulders whether she was comfortable.

Now she stretched herself: 'Pooh! The heat coming in through the window — it's like when you open an oven. It's really wearing me down. And how empty the country is! Where are your famous herds of camels? And people too? — I've only seen a few.'

'Many of the camels have made the journey to the butcher's and then into people's stomachs,' my uncle replied with a laugh, then tried to soothe Silvia's obvious disappointment: 'But there are still plenty left to do the ploughing. May Allah only give us some rain.'

It was well past noon when the date palms of Marrakech came to meet us. We passed quickly through the orderly European quarter, as it took its siesta, and drove into the teeming life of the main city. The crowds of walkers in those streets without pavements at the side engulfed our car like a fast-flowing stream. The nearness of doorless shops, the shouts and talk, and the familiar smell of spice, dust and mint put me in a tender mood.

We arrived at the small square, and from there a narrow alley took us to my father's house. The moment we were out of the car, we were surrounded by a swarm of little boys: my relatives waiting for us. The boys rushed off shouting to announce our arrival. Silvia followed me along the vaulted alley, stumbling at the depression which had been trodden into its centreline, a feature so familiar to me. After we had come round a few more bends, we were facing the wall of the house where I was born.

The door was slightly open. I led Silvia by the hand through the zigzagging hallway to the patio with its bright freshly chalked walls and its elegant fountain covered with mosaic. The place was swarming with women. All my female relatives and their children were there to welcome me: my brothers' wives, my cousins, aunts and great-aunts, and the servants. They were all in caftans, their hair covered with kerchiefs, and with bare feet because of the warm weather.

My mother was standing there too, calm as ever, a gentle smile playing on her light-skinned, pockmarked face. I made my way through the throng towards her, and covered her hair with kisses. The other women were eager to crowd round me to give their greetings, yet they remained motionless as if riveted to the ground. Their glances were directed at the hallway opening where Silvia had stopped. I motioned to her to come forward. Click-click-click, went her high heels as she crossed the mosaic amid the general silence. My mother kissed Silvia on both cheeks. The others followed her example, stiffly and cautiously, and then congregated keenly around me. Tears of joy trickled down the wrinkled cheeks of the mulatto Mbarka who had been purchased to do kitchen work back in the days of slavery. Great-aunt Zineb, a golden-hearted person, whispered to me:

'How delicate and beautiful your bride is, just like fine wheat flour! And we'll do a good job at dyeing her faded hair a nice black.'

I shook my head heatedly in disagreement, and at once she looked sad and hurt, with bewilderment in her eyes.

Happy as a king, I took off my shoes to step on the rug in the chamber. Silvia and I were seated in the place of honour, facing the open door. The women gradually entered, and seemed to form themselves into a garland on the circular sofa. Although all kept politely silent, I sensed a certain disquiet under their dignified composure. Silvia smiled awkwardly to right and left.

Deep down I chuckled, knowing that every tiny detail about Silvia was being noted by my relatives from underneath their half-lowered lids. The servant girl Tammou alone could not control herself. With a tea kettle hanging over her arm, she stationed herself in front of Silvia, open-mouthed, voraciously drinking in her dress, hands and shoes until my mother appeared in the doorway and called her to order. The tension evaporated only when the tea trays were placed on the rug and aromatic mint tea was poured out.

'Who is this wide-eyed girl on the left, the one with a pink tulle crown on her head?' Silvia asked in a low voice.

'My brother's wife.'

'And the one next to her, also in a pink caftan but with the child in her lap?'

'The same brother's second wife.'

'He has two wives?' Silvia raised her eyebrows.

'Yes, indeed — he has two.'

'Do all your brothers have two wives?'

'No. Two have two, and the third has only one.'

After tea, they wanted to separate Silvia from me immediately: it was not proper for the bride and the groom to sit together. However, noticing Silvia's unease, I imposed my will so that she should have lunch with me right there. The crowd left the room.

The low table was rolled in, and Silvia looked for knives and forks, but in vain. Obediently she dipped her piece of bread into the sauce in the dish. She seemed to like the food — how could she not like it?

But then they really put an end to our illicit cooing. The male relatives were waiting to enter the house. It was time for the women to move out.

Late in the evening I slipped out from the male circle and crossed the patio to find Silvia. A few female relatives were snoozing along the walls, and some had already stretched out for the night. Silvia alone was sitting somewhat stiffly on the furthest sofa, her suitcase beside her. When she saw me, she jumped to her feet, obviously with relief.

'Mohammed, please tell them to show me to my room. It is getting late.'

'But my love, you already are on your couch,' I explained.

She looked around uncomprehendingly, nodding meaningfully towards the reclining sheet-covered sleepers.

'Yes, Silvia,' I smiled. 'Here everything takes place in a cosy family way. See, Mother has provided this gorgeous embroidered sheet for you to cover yourself. You just lie down and go to sleep.'

'Where will I undress?'

That was a more ticklish question. In our house we spent the night in part of our daytime clothes, in line with the good old custom. So, for the first night, I just suggested that she unbutton the tightest things she was wearing.

I had handed Silvia over to our women and knew that as the groom I had no rights over her. Yet I broke the custom next morning by stealing into her room for a few minutes. I found her rested and smiling. She made a comic gesture of massaging the nape of her neck.

'Would it be possible to get hold of a feather pillow for tonight?' she asked. 'Your pillows here feel more like blocks of concrete.'

I looked at the cushions leaning against the wall, all of them equally large and tightly filled with wool. I was reminded of my first encounter with a feather pillow in Europe and the insidious way its fluffy mass cheated my head's need for support. No, ours were trustworthy pillows, but Silvia's wish could be accommodated.

I was on my way out when Silvia rather bashfully pulled me by the sleeve:

. 'The lavatory has run out of paper. Would you mind asking your mother . . .'

Run out? I did not know how to react. On reflection I decided not to explain now that up to now this house had made do with water, soap and a towel — and that one had one's own small flat stone for the rest of the job. But, of course, the new age demanded paper as well.

In the course of the next day, Silvia found much beauty and originality in our house. She was in raptures over the carved-wood ceilings and the gypsum lace on the walls. She passed a caressing hand over the mosaic panels and stroked the plush sofas. She had also become familiar with the kitchen where the women ('God knows when I'll work out who's who!') were preparing food and cleaning vegetables on a reed mat on the floor. She told me about the kettles and clay dishes simmering and bubbling underneath an enormously high open chimney. She had also been taken to a smaller side patio which felt more like a well because at that point the house had two floors. The children had dashed around them like ants. Everything was carefully explained to her, but she had not understood a word.

'That's where my brothers live.'

'You mentioned some time ago about plans to have a house built for us too. A villa in the European quarter, I trust.'

I could not resist the temptation to give Silvia a pleasant surprise right now, even before the wedding:

'It's done! The house next door. Your house-hunting worries are over. I'll show it to you as soon as I have a moment.'

The moment did not come all that soon. To please my family I let the old tradition prevail, and stopped my visits to Silvia. She must rest and recuperate. I was living in my own home, only a stone's throw away, surrounded during the day-time and often at night too by friends. I met my mother at my brothers' house.

Knowing that Silvia was in Mother's excellent hands, I could abandon myself to the full enjoyment of the atmosphere of my native land. In the rooms, free from European furniture and bric-à-brac, one could stretch one's limbs. And the open sky overhead in the patio made it easier to breathe. It was so delightful living cheek-by-jowl with one's own people. The children, those jokers, were all over the place, and they were in the habit of grabbing at my trouser legs. The total for my three brothers and the two patios of our house could well be close to twenty if one started counting them up.

I asked Mother how Silvia was acclimatising herself. 'That I can not ask her. I don't speak her language.' Her voice had a melancholy undertone, but she went on calmly: 'Don't you worry, my son. We'll take good care that the evil eye does not strike your bride and that Those Other Beings do her no harm.' Of course, Mother was referring to the underground house spirits; belief in their existence had lately tailed off, but it had not completely disappeared. Why risk insulting those temperamental spirits? One had to be particularly careful at the time of a wedding, because they loved to play dangerous tricks on the bride.

When I visited Silvia again a week later, I was surprised to find her out of sorts. She said how isolated she felt in a house without outside windows, and complained of being bored, and that I was leaving her alone all the time. She said she wanted to go out with me and see the city. Of course, Morocco already had many brides and grooms taking walks together. Girls had begun to attend school with their faces uncovered, and the first small group of college-educated girls had even set out to found a women's league. But the old customs still had not been abandoned in our household. So I did not think it was appropriate for Silvia to leave the house during her bridal period.

Still, I sneaked to her after lunch the following day while everyone else was taking a siesta. At least Silvia could have the diversion of seeing our new house!

We did not even have to go out into the street. A twisting corridor took us straight there. The patio was spacious, and its walls were covered all over with multi-coloured tiles, which were still rough from recent cement work. There were two rooms facing each other. Proudly I pulled open the door of the one that Mother had furnished: a red carpet lined with iridescent red-and-white plush mattresses. The other room was empty. I prudently forbore to tell Silvia that its furnishing would normally have come from the bride's dowry. Silvia had come empty-handed. There we could install a European-style bed, table and chairs. I expected a burst of enthusiasm, but Silvia was silent.

'And the kitchen?' she inquired in a matter-of-fact tone. When she learned that we would share the general family kitchen, her head dropped.

I had something more to show her. When my father was still among the living, he had wanted to surprise me by installing a modern bathtub. It was displayed in a special room at the end of a passage. I had to smile sentimentally: the brave Arab master-craftsmen had built this luxurious object long and high like a citadel. A cold water tap had been built into the wall.

Returning to the patio, Silvia stopped and looked mutely up to the hot leaden patch of sky above. Shrugging her shoulders helplessly, she observed:

'It has no windows.'

'What do you mean: no windows?' I said, pointing to the four room windows opening on the patio.

'Those don't count!' she said. Her mood brightening up, she went into the empty room and put her hand on the outer wall.

'Look,' she said with determination, 'we'll cut a window here!'

The proposal was so grotesque that I burst out laughing. I pictured our city quarter with alleys that are only a step and a half wide and absolutely windowless façades suddenly sprouting a window in our house wall, with passers-by congregating in front of it as if it were a movie screen! I patted Silvia on the shoulder to calm her, but my amiable gesture made her mad. She stamped on the ground.

'I don't care for a house with no windows!' she shouted, then, joined her two hands around her neck: 'Don't you understand, your windowless rooms are choking me!'

Afraid that she might burst out crying, I quickly took her back to my mother.

The wedding day was getting near. The women were busy. Sewing machines rattled. My uncle had the full responsibility for stocking up with food: grinding the grain, buying the sheep and the few hundred chickens, procuring the incense and spices. The festive reception for the notary took place in my uncle's house where the marriage contract was drawn up. The wedding feast was also to be at my uncle's, since his house was new and refined. The patio floor was paved with marble tiles, and the columns at the entrances to the rooms had shiny brass grids. In the middle of the yard my uncle had built a round podium about a metre high, covered with mosaic and flowers. It was surrounded by a narrow aquarium where fish swam under frosted glass.

Silvia soon moved to the wedding house where she received a small chamber facing the main patio. In this private room she could have a brief respite and pull back into her European shell before the wedding day — which, of course, she had to spend in the main living room, where a corner had been set apart for her with a roll of cloth. Behind this curtain Silvia was safe from the evil eye. In that warm nest she could quietly and happily spend the obligatory seven days, never once setting foot outside. The nights there would belong to the two of us. I would spend the days with friends in a neighbour's house — that was the custom.

I was told that Silvia had already been taken to the baths several times in a row. Cost what it might, I had to see her once more before the wedding night. She came to meet me, a kerchief over her hair.

'You are already adopting some of this country's ways,' I said tenderly and approvingly.

She bit her lip and lowered her glance. Then she tore off the kerchief:

'Just look!'

My eyes bulged.

'Why, your hair is red like . . .'

'Yes, like carrots,' she tartly finished the sentence.

She had discovered the change after her latest visit to the baths, when she had been rubbed all over with a spinach-like mush which made her skin smooth. Unsuspectingly, she had allowed them to put mush on her hair too.

'That's henna,' I explained. 'Crushed henna leaves. They give black hair a nice copper shine. My people could not know that your blond hair is so sensitive.'

I seized her hands: 'You know, Silvia, henna brings luck. What kind of bride would you be if you were not hennaed? Now everything is in order, you are my darling hennaed princess.'

She smiled faintly. The pink hair made her face look pale. But, in any case, she had become paler during the last few weeks.

The wedding day came. Although there were numerous male guests who filled the entire house, their feeding proceeded smoothly and swiftly under my uncle's watchful eye. My role as groom was to help the servants as they carried the dishes to the guests.

The next day, women took charge of the house. Their rule usually lasted for seven days. They started to arrive early in the morning, each carrying a locked bag containing several wedding gowns. Around noon I cast a sinful male glance towards the patio from the second floor of my uncle's house. It was bright with

women's gowns — the living rooms must have been over-
flowing. Crammed against each other, they sat cross-legged on
the carpets. The weather was oppressively hot and the sun was
scorching, so all the available space close to the wall was occupied
by those seeking refuge in its shadow.

I hurried back to the company of my friends at the house next
door. We had not yet started lunch when my uncle came excitedly
looking for me. Something unheard-of had happened: taking the
law into her own hands, Silvia had come out from her bridal
corner pen!

To the consternation of my family she had refused to use the
chamber pot that had been handed to her behind her curtain and
had gone to the lavatory instead. Having visited that place
swarming with house spirits and thus so dangerous for a bride, she
walked quite calmly through the crowd of appalled guests to her
own everyday room. She had indicated to my mother that the
thick caftans had made her sweat. At the insistence of my people
she had finally agreed to return to the living room corner.

That was quite a story! I could well imagine all the disapproval
and the guests' tongues wagging. For my part there was no way I
could go and explain the situation either to Silvia or to the wedding guests. Men had absolutely no right of entry to the wedding
house. And would my people have understood me anyway, those
who had so solicitously tried to protect Silvia against all evil by
hanging Koranic verses in her bride's corner? As for Silvia, she
would have been even less inclined to take me seriously. Perhaps it
was I who had not done the job of preparing her thoroughly
enough?

Among friends I soon forgot what had happened. We ate and
drank, then played cards, to the accompaniment of music. In the
afternoon my uncle appeared once more, but this time he smiled
and was in a good mood. Enigmatically, he asked me to come
along, and guided me again up his private entrance to his second-
floor chamber. From there one had a wonderful view of the patio.
The floor seemed to be entirely covered in shiny silk and glittering
gold. A fly could not have found a resting space there. Silvia must
be proud to have such a wedding! True, it had become almost

impossible for the servants to pass through with their trays of food, as they vainly tried to find space among the sitting women to set down their feet. The flat roof of the house was completely full too. These were the uninvited guests who had pushed their way in through the kitchen and gone up the stairs, driven by curiosity to see the foreign bride. Indeed the hour had come to present the bride to the guests.

The strident '*yu-yu*' screams filled my ears. Flanked by two matrons and guided by both hands, Silvia made her appearance. Was this queen from the Thousand and One Nights really her? The wide-sleeved golden gown extended to the floor. Jewels covered her shoulders and chest, on her head was a golden crown, and her face was framed by strings of pearls. Majestically she glided to the podium, her eyes tightly shut, and there she was assisted, using a stool, to climb up to the seat of honour in the midst of flowers. The house rang with shouts of greeting.

As if bewitched, I feasted my eyes on Silvia. A tremor of joy gripped my heart, and I wished I could prostrate myself at her feet in adoration. How long did she sit there, her mouth flushed like a poppy and her eyes strictly closed? Probably not for long. The matrons soon heaved her to her feet, and many arms offered the stool for her to step down again.

Then it happened. There was a clatter of broken glass and a cry from Silvia. She had stepped past the stool and fallen straight into the aquarium.

Confusion and noise became indescribable. I saw Silvia's leg with blood on it. I went storming downstairs like a madman and banged my fists on the door, but the women would not open it under any condition. Even when the physician had arrived, having been summoned by phone, it took a stern order from my uncle to have the door opened. Some guests still rebuffed us, shouting nastily: 'Out with the men!' But nothing could stop the two of us from ploughing our way through the mass of women, mercilessly stepping on their crossed legs. At last, we reached Silvia's room.

My mother helped Silvia to discard the jewellery and so did my aunts, who looked particularly smitten by fate, with reproach in their eyes. The house spirits and the evil eye had won. Silvia's calf had a deep longitudinal cut.

She sobbed:

'How did I know where to step, with eyes closed?'

'But you were told there was glass in front of you.'

'Oh God! You know perfectly well that I don't understand what they say. How can you reproach me like that?'

Inside the room, I leaned my back heavily against the door to prevent the women from rushing in. The physician proceeded with his task, and Silvia gradually became quieter.

'Please be reasonable,' I said in a purposely severe tone. 'Soon it will be night, and then I'll come and join you.'

'And then we'll go away?' she asked eagerly.

I did not answer. What could I have said? The wedding feast was to go on, in exactly the same way, for another seven days. On the last day the young wife would be begirded and could then emerge from her corner into her new life. And I knew too that I would not be allowed to join Silvia before the cock had crowed. That was what custom dictated.

'Never mind, the leg will heal sure enough,' my friends said encouragingly. 'Drink and build up your strength. The wedding night is ahead of you — you must perform like a man!'

Having clothed me in white and set me like a sultan in the centre, they played at being my court ministers. At nightfall I was taken to the baths, and the family barber shaved me and sprinkled me with rose water. Certain spices were cunningly mixed with my food to enhance my manhood.

I felt charged with electricity and full of enterprising spirit when a candle guided me to my bride in my uncle's house. Silvia must be awaiting me in happy anticipation in her bridal corner!

The corner pen was vacant. Silvia had stayed in her chamber.

She was sleepy. Seeing me as I approached, she got up from her couch and yawned, dragging her wounded leg:

'I feel dead. Why did you take so long? I began to think you weren't coming at all.'

I started hugging her, but she drew away:

'Let us leave this place! I don't want to be here any longer.'

In my impatience I felt offended. I pulled her to my side on the sofa:

'What is enticing you away from here? Wasn't everything offered to you and done in the way I promised it would?'

'All that, and more. Too much more! But look . . . I don't know how to tell you this . . .'

Suddenly all her languor vanished, and she spoke with a fierce intensity:

'I am not yet used to showing my emotions to the entire city. And even less . . . even less can I bear the thought of my wedding pants being flaunted tomorrow morning in front of everyone, as your custom is here!'

The next moment she threw her arms around my neck:

'Come on, let's leave this place! Let's get out now! I beg you, Mohammed, I beg you!'

I lost my head.

Right, we would go! Where to? One of my friends had a place outside the city, and his family had gone away for the summer. We would go there.

I went straight to plead with my uncle, and came back with his car keys.

We fled, upsetting all the wedding celebrations. Only far away from there did we find each other. But how will I ever bridge the chasm that our rash action has created between me and my own utterly offended people?

THE NAME-GIVING CEREMONY
(1960)

Lalla Maria, still very young, gave birth to her first child — not at her husband Sidi Omar's home but at her father's. Consequently her father was entitled to arrange for the name-giving ceremony at his house. I was told to be there by noon.

Poor Lalla Ghita. If things had only worked out right, it was she who should have been a mother, for had she not been Sidi Omar's wife for a full three years? But she could not get a child. Allah had not entered any children in her book of fate.

So the only course left for the husband was to bring a second wife to the house to complement Ghita. That second one turned out to be Lalla Maria, Ghita's very own uncle's daughter. And lo and behold, Lalla Maria completed her task right away within nine months, though unfortunately in the form of a daughter rather than a son.

The windowless façade of the house of celebration was the usual one for Marrakech. The front door was closed. The house was probably bursting with male guests waiting for the festive noon-time meal. And once the men had left, the women would spread into the entire house in their dazzling floor-length brocade and tinsel caftans. But because the afternoon was short, women were often assigned the whole next day for their meeting. This is how celebrations had been organised for centuries, and Lalla Maria's father certainly did not intend to follow the foolish modern custom of throwing men and women together. I had been asked to come early, probably so that I could spend some hours with the women of the house before the female guests arrived.

I entered and passed along the twisting hallway past the stairs leading to the upper floor. To my surprise I found the patio deserted; no one was to be seen. Hesitantly, I went to the wide-open door of the living room and cautiously looked in. Wasn't this where the men were meeting? The room was empty. The women would of course be in the women's chamber at the oppo-

200

site end of the patio. This was where Lalla Maria was supposed to
lie after the birth. I was brought up short at the threshold: this
room was empty too. The young mother and all the other women
seemed to have vanished into thin air.

What was it all about? Had I come on the wrong day? Yet it
certainly was the seventh day after the birth and thus the obligatory day for name-giving. Where was everybody? We were not in
Europe where the whole household would have gone to church
for the christening.

Miriam, the black servant girl, with her dishevelled head and
rolling eyes, appeared in the kitchen hallway. She was smiling,
and her finger pointed upwards: go to the second floor.

Returning to the hallway I ran into a group of men in fluffy
white burnouses — apparently the first male visitors. Their
glances passed over me, a female, very politely but as if I were not
there. I quickly stepped out of their way, and took the stairs to the
upper part of the house.

A servant's arms seized me as I came to the final steps and pulled
me on to the balcony. For this occasion it was sheltered by a cloth
that had been rigged up from floor to ceiling to hide the women.
The sky was cloudy, and its indifferent light was filtered through
the cloth. The chamber behind the balcony was almost in darkness.

Only very few women sat in the room, slumbering in a row,
their heads thrown back against the wall. There was Sidi Omar's
dark-skinned sister, Lalla Hadoush, fat and shapeless, the oldest
of the ladies. Next to her were two female relatives and a girl called
Naima. At one end of the room, barely distinguishable in the
gloom, was a curved recumbent figure — the young mother,
Lalla Maria. Her baby daughter was probably hidden by her side.
And wasn't that Lalla Ghita huddled up in the corner, a kerchief
drawn deep down over her eyes?

Several questions were on my mind, but something made me
hesitate before saying anything to Lalla Hadoush. On earlier occasions too, I had felt inhibited by her majestic corpulence, and now
particularly the insistent glance of her deep-set eyes under their
beetling brows restrained me. I knew that this person of few

words was accustomed to giving orders. So I struck up a quiet conversation with Naima.

'Did you take the mother and the child to the baths at the proper evening hours?'

'We certainly did. Lalla Maria's father rented the baths for the whole night. It was dawn by the time we got back.'

'Will there be many female guests today?'

'Not a single one. Today is men's day. Women's day will be tomorrow.'

'Where is the mistress of the house?'

'Sitting in the storeroom.'

'And the other ladies of the house?'

'Helping the servants in the kitchen.'

Lalla Naima yawned, then quickly slammed her palm over her mouth so that the evil spirits could not slip into her throat.

So the mistress was in the storeroom. I knew this shack in the patio near the open-air kitchen. It was rather a wall cupboard, and its floor could hold one woman spread out on a sheepskin or three sitting cross-legged. On the men's day, when it was not becoming for women to be seen, this place had the crucial function of a general headquarters from which the mistress of the house could direct and supervise the workforce mobilised in the kitchen and elsewhere. From it she slipped into the kitchen and back again, covered by her blanket, and when she was inside it she would peer out and grab the servants who were waiting on men by the flap, to ask for news. The storeroom became a sort of a post-office to which notes and information were dispatched and from which orders were sent out.

The room I was in had none of the animation about it which one normally associated with a festivity. What fun could there be for women on a men's day? For the housewives it meant only work and bustling. Those who had no actual tasks to perform in this house, apart from hiding themselves, could merely relax and sleep. So they slumbered in silence. At times, the fat Lalla Hadoush glanced inquisitively at Ghita. Was she asleep, or had she hidden herself, along with her thoughts, behind her kerchief? Why wasn't she even pregnant when her co-wife was already at the name-giving stage? Was she to become a scorned childless woman whom every husband tried to get rid of? True, Sidi Omar was not likely to behave like that. He was a worthy man. Besides, Ghita had kinship ties with Maria. The course of her future life was known only to Allah in His might and to the angel Gabriel who was in charge of the entries in Allah's book of fates. It would have been extremely sinful to whine and whimper rather than submit to Allah's will with a calm heart. On the ground floor the ladies of the house had no time for slumber. The headquarters was alert and active. Less than half an hour passed before the servant Miriam appeared before our half-closed eyes, carrying a tray with steaming tea glasses on her head.

'Eh, Lalla Ghita, tea has arrived!' Lalla Hadoush called out in her resonant bass voice. Ghita was handed a glass, and she obediently started to sip. No one disturbed the young mother. Pampering her would come later.

A few gulps of mint tea woke me up. With the glass in my hand, I went to the balcony, pulled off a flap of the canvas attached to a pillar, and squatted down. How nice and free it felt to be on the lookout here after the somnolent atmosphere of the chamber! Soft light from the cloudy sky filled the patio, where the walls looked so clean and white. The black and white floor tiles ran round the walls and crossed the patio in two ways, at right angles, with the fountain's marble basin occupying the centre. In the four quadrants thus delineated, orange trees were in full bloom. It was April, and flowers of many colours surrounded the trees. The mint aroma in my glass mixed with the strong scent of orange flowers. Only the bird-cherry blossom in my Estonian homeland could compete with orange blossom in causing a yearning anxiety.

The patio was deserted. White figures could be seen through the arched door of the living room — the male guests I had encountered earlier. Their heelless yellow slippers stood guard at the threshold.

Suddenly there was a stir in the patio. Five musicians with instruments entered through the hallway door. In no time a servant was there and spread a rug on the tiles of the garden path. The musicians sat down cross-legged and set themselves up. Violins were tuned. Guests started to arrive singly and in groups. The host, Lalla Maria's father, was among them. The men had apparently just returned from noontime prayers at the mosque. The row of yellow slippers near the door became noticeably longer. As the guests settled themselves in the living room and the servants started to dart across the patio with tea trays, the musicians filled the air with impetuous song, swinging violin rhythms and the jangle of drums.

Another peculiar row had formed in the patio, starting from the kitchen and extending along the wall, this time of round clay dishes, each covered with a glazed brown clay cone. There were nine of them. Although they were waiting to be served, there was no risk of the food spoiling or becoming congealed, because in clay dishes fat will bubble for a long time. Near the fountain, appetisers — in the shape of *bastila* pies the size of cartwheels — were shown off in boxes covered with velvet-covered cones.

As the men began to eat, I felt a hand on my shoulder. It was Lalla Ghita. She glanced past me.

'Quite a row of dishes,' I remarked.

'We will have no fewer tomorrow at our house,' she replied. 'Sidi Omar feels happy to hear the sounds of a baby in the house. Yes, the women's celebration tomorrow will be at our home, not here.'

Somehow the way she spoke was unnaturally placid. She squatted in front of me. Her face was very light and round, exactly as a face should be to earn praise and be compared to a full moon according to the Moroccan code of beauty. But she lacked animation; there was something somnolent about her features. Did it denote resignation? I visualised Lalla Maria's elongated and slightly brownish face, her bright young girl's eyes, and her sparkling smile which revealed two golden eyeteeth. Yes, her future seemed assured. Yet Lalla Ghita was still young too.

'How old are you?' I asked.

'I was born during the last onslaught of the locusts.'

That, I calculated, must have been twenty-two or twenty-three years ago. But already her expression was that of a mature, even a long-suffering woman.

'Do you get on well with Lalla Maria?'

'Yes,' she replied brusquely, but then added with a certain pride: 'We stem from the same family tree.'

I did not take her 'yes' at face value. In every country family members quarrel more with each other than with friends. One can choose one's friends, while our family is imposed on us. However, in Morocco kinship ties are paramount, and because the two co-wives were cousins, the bitterest feuds would certainly be avoided in Sidi Omar's house.

Downstairs the men seemed in an unusual hurry as they ate their meal. What was the rush today? The servants bustled around, carrying the heavy dishes in and out. The row of clay pots waiting their turn got shorter, and when the last one had gone and the tea trays reappeared, the women also received some food. Miriam carried up a dish that is cooked especially for women on the occasion of a name-giving. It consisted of the liver, brains and kidneys of a sheep — in short everything that Allah had given the sheep apart from its meat for enjoyment by humans.

We washed our hands and barely had time to dip for morsels in the hot sauce, using our fingers and pieces of bread, when a sheep's bleating was heard downstairs.

'It's going to happen now,' Naima pushed me with her elbow. 'Go and take a look. The child is going to receive its name.'

Hurriedly I licked my greasy fingers clean. This had to be seen! I looked down into the patio. Near the fountain a large woolly sheep stood apparently huddled against the butcher. Maria's little brother happily patted its head. Further away, so that they could not be overheard, Maria's father and uncle whispered with Sidi Omar, heads close together. Those three scholars and servants of Allah, who had been on the pilgrimage to Mecca, did not have to follow the usual practice of drawing lots in order to determine the child's name. No, those privileged ones could simply confer and agree on a name. Their conference was a short one. Soon a signal was given to those in the room, and the men streamed out of the door as if it were a mosque, each one busy looking for his slippers and putting them on.

An aged cantor stepped forward. He began chanting verses from the Koran and the others joined in. The sheep was frightened by its strange situation and, as if scenting danger, made an attempt to pull itself loose. But the butcher held it fast and broke its front leg bone with a cracking noise.

The animal collapsed like a pile of wool, but none the less managed to get up again, panting. Crack! the butcher broke its other front leg. In crazed panic the animal crawled along on its two broken stumps. It reeled over, heaved itself up, then collapsed again. Trembling, it tried once more to get up, but the hands of the butcher and his aids were quickly upon it. The sheep was turned over on its back like a bundle. The cantor raised his dagger: 'In the name of gracious and merciful Allah, who has created you, I name you . . .' The child's name was drowned in the storm of chanting and the sound of musical instruments. I closed my European eyes.

When I dared to open them again, blood was gushing over the white marble of the fountain, and the sheep lay motionless. But as if to show that earthly life will resist death to the last, the sheep suddenly jumped, thrashed around, tried to get up, fell again, and twitched. Every muscle and sinew, every tuft of wool was crying out mutely in this final agony.

At last it looked vanquished and dead, but not yet — its entire vital force gathered in a terrible effort which launched its body up in the air, as if riding a hurricane, to land in the hollow of the fountain, and there it remained. Only now had it stopped being a sheep and become meat.

I turned away. Lalla Ghita was leaning against the door jamb. Her lips moved in prayer. The young mother had also pulled herself up, and walked the few steps to the balustrade, where she glanced through the slit at the canvas edge. I supported her when she returned to the couch. Her aunt came up the stairs. Beaming, she announced the child's name in a loud voice:

'Latifa!'

Maria took the baby into her arms and looked at her in confusion. The child's eyelids and brows were blackened with kohl to strengthen her vision. So her name was Latifa . . .

At once the aunt seized the child, threw a bath towel over her, and took her down the stairs. In the lobby she placed the baby in the arms of a servant, all the while covering the child's face so that the evil eye could not impinge on it.

As the servant stepped among the male visitors, each one of them took a folded banknote held in reserve and stuck it under the child.

Soon after that, the guests departed. Our meal continued, but my appetite was gone. The mutton dishes had lost their attraction. Forcing myself to chew, I reproached myself for my excessive sensibility: what was one sheep more or less, and even its bones would have remained unbroken if only the butcher had had a professional assistant with him. Were there not sheep carcasses hanging everywhere in rows facing the butcher shops? And did the sheep remain unslaughtered on Estonian farms? The women I was facing ate with gusto. Those sober children of nature were used to seeing sheep killed frequently since early youth. Ghita looked tired and pale, her few freckles standing out sharply. Her eyes were small, oily and expressionless. Dark shadows formed below their vacant gaze.

As the meal ended, it was my turn to leave. I was quite puzzled when Lalla Hadoush, still sitting cross-legged, offered to escort me to the front door, taking the place of the exhausted mistress of the house. Getting to her feet was a problem for her. With much effort she stretched out her legs, rolled sideways on to her arm, used both hands to turn herself to face the couch, puffing all the time, and only then succeeded in getting up. She signalled Ghita to follow us.

When we reached the lobby, Lalla Hadoush did not even notice my outstretched hand. Instead, she seized Lalla Ghita by the shoulders.

'Lalla Ghita!' she said severely in her deep voice. 'Listen to what I have to tell you. Latifa will become your child. Yes, that sheep was sacrificed in the name of your child. Don't bulge your eyes — Allah willing, my lips are telling you the truth. Lalla Maria will give birth to still other children, with Allah's help, and Latifa will be your share. Let Maria breastfeed her, but you will tie her with a cloth to your back. Lull her to sleep during your daily work and at night on your couch. At first you will both take care of the child, until the next one is born. May Allah make it a boy. Let Latifa call you 'dear mother Lalla Ghita' just as she says 'dear mother Lalla Maria'. Her younger brothers and sisters will crowd around their mother, but Latifa is bound to attach herself to you. You are a kin of Lalla Maria, and it is the command of Allah and our kinship group to take from where there's excess and to give to those who lack. Latifa will grow up as a daughter for you. It's you who will give her in marriage and have grandmotherly enjoyment of her children.'

Ghita listened to this talk with her mouth open. As she stood there, with a slightly idiotic expression, Lalla Hadoush's fingers dug deeper in her shoulders, and suddenly she gave her such a violent shake that Ghita's head banged against the wall.

'You don't understand, do you?' Lalla Hadoush was almost shouting. 'Latifa is yours.'

Lalla Ghita seemed to waken from torpor. She went slowly up the stairs. As she reached the top, she turned, waved good-bye to me, and called out:

'You will come tomorrow, will you?'

A smile played on her lips.

'*Inshallah!*' I promised.

SUCH A CUSTOM MUST BE ABOLISHED

(1970)

The recently widowed Lalla Rahalia had come to visit the wife of the *adoul* (notary), at whose house I happened to meet her in the *kouba*, or women's room. In only a short time, she had aged noticeably. Somehow, her face had shrunk and narrowed; one front tooth was missing, and the hair dangling from underneath her scarf showed signs of grey despite the reddish henna dye.

'How are things?' I inquired. She made a gesture of despair.

'How can things be? Life with all those co-wives was complicated enough even before his death, but now it's utterly crazy. You don't know any longer whether you are going to have anything to eat or not. They are like hounds around you, one trying to seize whatever she can, another ready to scratch your eyes out.'

Lalla Mina, sitting with her little son in her lap, nodded. She was one of the three daughters-in-law of the notary's wife. All three lived in the house with their husbands. A recent attack of pneumonia had made Lalla Mina's beautiful black eyes still larger and more expressive.

'Hah, those men,' she said, saying the word with her customary smile, and as calmly as if the topic were utterly casual and inconsequential. Yet everyone in the room knew that Mina's whole internal world had collapsed on the day during her illness when her husband had married an additional wife, renting a separate house for her.

'What is a woman to the man? Absolutely nothing . . .' Lalla Mina added, as if in a dream. Lalla Rahalia was rocking the upper part of her body.

'There's no repose, that's the thing. You get no rest and quiet while your husband is alive, and none even when he's dead. This whole life and existence is an impossible salad.'

Lalla Mina raised her eyebrows and exclaimed:

'Salad? How right you are! A salad.' Her chin motioned

209

toward the second daughter-in-law of the notary's wife, sitting
opposite. 'See? Is it any better with them? Since Sidi Said added
that other one, what has become of your life, Lalla Fatima? A
salad.'

The room fell silent. For the sake of diversion, I commented:

'A man is constantly looking for variety. When his wife is
pregnant or ill, he will look for someone to amuse him. But later
he will spend his time with the one who is more fun, who laughs
more — you, Lalla Mina, are pretty good at that.'

Lalla Mina began to laugh, indeed, but she did so only briefly,
with scorn. Then she said firmly:

'Whether you laugh or don't laugh, it's all the same. We have
laughed for the last time. Now it's too late.' She repeated, in an
inflexible tone: 'Too late.'

Lalla Rahalia quickly added:

'It's the man who will have the last laugh. Our laughter is
quickly over. How can you laugh when your liver has become as
hard as coal?'

'Who are the people that are living with you now?' I asked.

'Well, my son Rahal is here under our roof, and his wife. She
already has a small girl. An affectionate line could be seen
fleetingly, before her mouth hardened again. 'Then there is that
other one with her two sons and three daughters, and now that
most recent one . . .' now her eyes were really vicious . . . 'with
her two brats.' She struck sharply at her knee, exclaiming: 'The
property has to be divided up. It cannot go on like this. The houses
and landholdings exist, but my husband's brothers are making
money out of them, and they don't want to go ahead with
dividing them up, claiming to be our guardians. Nothing
doing — there must be a division, and everyone will get his
share!'

There was an uneasy silence again. Then suddenly, as one
looked at Lalla Mina's madonna-like face, her teeth flashed:

'How wonderful it would be if one were a man. Money . . .
women. . . .'

'But you have children,' I interjected.

'Children?' She looked into the distance, and the corners of her mouth dropped. 'Today I have them, tomorrow maybe not. . . .'

I remembered another young woman, who had also lived in this house: the daughter of the matron's brother-in-law.

'How is Lalla Zhamila doing?'

'*Shuyya* . . . so-so,' the matron replied.

'How is her husband's health?'

I knew that Hadj Mohammed was dying. Cancer was eating away the body of this husband, who was over eighty. Even about ten years ago, when I attended his wedding with Lalla Zhamila, he was already venerable, with a grey beard. Lalla Zhamila was an innocent fifteen-year-old bride in full flower.

By habit, the lady of the house gave the instant ready-made reply, obligatory in the case of any and all inquiries about health:

'*Shuyya. . . .*'

She continued staring straight to her front. Her head started to droop, as if she felt only exhaustion. But she rallied at once, and when she spoke, her voice was completely altered.

'No, it is not good that a young girl should be selected for a husband older than her own father. This really is not good. Such a custom must be abolished! Zhamila is still so young; how is she to live after the death of her husband? Stay bundled together with his older wives and their children? But if she were to remarry, all those sons and daughters of the other wives will say: 'Aha! You are squandering our father's property with another man! Aren't you ashamed?'

I looked at the mistress of the house with new curiosity. Was this still that meek, equable and deeply religious notary's spouse, who had never said no to anything or anyone, who was now daring to speak in such a way? It must be some totally different person sitting there before me, a modern woman. Was this evolution in her thinking the result of living in common with the wives of her three sons who made her recall vividly the experiences, the chagrin of her own youth? Hadn't she only recently confided to me: my husband is now old; Evil Spirits have vacated his physical body. I sensed that over the years new ideas had begun to take shape in the mind of this outwardly traditional, but wise woman, ideas about the insecure and troubled existence of women —

until, slowly, she had come to a clear realisation that something was wrong, that something in women's existence was not as it should be.

The notary's senior wife was certainly not challenging polygamy — one had to submit humbly, with bended knee, to the commands of God and the prophets — but it was all too apparent that she had pondered the question of why women were obliged to spend their short lives on such shaky ground. Why did they have to share their home and rights with co-wives, competing with each other for the husband's affection, in unseemly scrimmages that no one could avoid? Didn't men all too often act selfishly and thoughtlessly, when they procured ever more wives for themselves? Why did they not stop to consider the consequences and imagine the women's feelings, instead of merely giving in to their own passions, as if this were a matter of course?

All these questions, which had accumulated over a long lifetime, had begun to ferment in the matron's mind. Now they erupted and it could all be expressed in a single sentence: such a custom had to be abolished! Lalla Rahalia was indeed right: peace and repose were what these women lacked. It certainly could not please Allah that people were squabbling and forever in a restless state. Centuries had gone by, times and conditions had changed, life had taken new forms. Emotions, too, needed to be reformed.

Her own husband was old. Who knows how many more days Allah would give him now? And then she would face a widow's existence, like Lalla Rahalia. None of her sons could fend for himself — they all depended on their father. And if the father should die, what trouble could come during the time that would follow his death? What would happen over the partition of the property, and what sort of a corner would she be able to find for herself where she could pass the time as she waited for the end of her life?

Everything proceeds from Allah. . . . What 'has been written' (in the heavenly book of fates) will happen, be it good or bad. Let us therefore go on living without worry, from day to day, up to the ultimate day when we will face Allah's judgment. . . .

The lady of the house was smiling again, amiable and congenial.

INDEX